G. W. BOWERS,

Dayton, *Wash.*

PENTECOSTAL HYMNS

No. 1

A WINNOWED COLLECTION

FOR

EVANGELISTIC SERVICES

YOUNG PEOPLE'S SOCIETIES

AND

SUNDAY-SCHOOLS

SELECTED BY
HENRY DATE

———

MUSIC EDITORS

E. A. HOFFMAN   W. A. OGDEN   J. H. TENNEY

———

PUBLISHED BY
THE HOPE PUBLISHING COMPANY
228 WABASH AVE., CHICAGO.

PREFATORY.

Pentecost was the peep of day.

Each dawn wakens melody; music dwells in light.

Nature hails every rising sun with a matin of praise.

There is a hallelujah chorus in every sunbeam, and an oratorio in every drop of dew the sun kisses.

Every heart from sin set free is a whispering gallery, wherein Purity walks and Hope sings.

Christianity will never fail while men and women pray, praise and practice.

Outbursts of song follow in the wake of showers of blessing.

Satan trembles whenever he visits a church where everybody sings.

The heart that cannot sing needs Christ.

A dumb pew makes a numb pulpit.

Let it not be forgotten that sin is a discordant note whose measure is eternity.

Holiness is a unison tone, whose time-beat is forever.

Years come and go, but "Peace on earth, good-will to men" is the song of ages.

Moses would have reached Canaan, had Miriam kept Israel singing.

No forward movement is possible where doubt stifles joy, and murmurings drown the voice of praise.

Salvation is not a dirge, but a resurrection doxology.

Henry Date.

Pentecostal Hymns.

1

More About Jesus.

E. E. HEWITT.   JNO. R. SWENEY.

1. More a-bout Je - sus would I know, More of his grace to oth-ers show;
2. More a-bout Je - sus let me learn, More of his ho - ly will dis-cern;
3. More a-bout Je - sus; in his Word, Holding communion with my Lord;
4. More a-bout Je - sus; on his throne, Rich-es in glo - ry all his own;

More of his sav - ing full-ness see, More of his love who died for me.
Spir - it of God, my teach-er be, Showing the things of Christ to me.
Hear-ing his voice in ev - 'ry line, Making each faith-ful say-ing mine.
More of his kingdom's sure increase; More of his coming, Prince of Peace.

REFRAIN.

More, more a - bout Je - sus, More, more a - bout Je - sus;

More of his sav - ing full-ness see, More of his love who died for me.

3

Throw out the Life-Line.

May be sung as a Solo and Chorus.

Rev. E. S. UFFORD.   E. S. U. Arr. by GEO. C. STEBBINS.

1. Throw out the Life-Line a-cross the dark wave, There is a broth-er whom
2. Throw out the Life-Line with hand quick and strong: Why do you tar - ry, why
3. Throw out the Life-Line to danger-fraught men, Sink-ing in anguish where
4. Soon will the sea - son of res - cue be o'er, Soon will they drift to e -

some one should save; Some-bod-y's broth-er! oh, who then, will dare To
lin - ger, so long? See! he is sink-ing; oh, hast-en to - day—And
you've nev-er been: Winds of tempt-a - tion and bil-lows of woe Will
ter - ni - ty's shore, Haste, then, my brother, no time for de - lay, But

CHORUS.

throw out the Life-Line, his per - il to share?
out with the Life-Boat! a - way, then, a - way!
soon hurl them out where the dark wa-ters flow.   Throw out the Life-Line!
throw out the Life-Line, and save them to - day.

Throw out the Life-Line! Some one is drift-ing a - way; Throw out the

Life-Line! Throw out the Life-Line! Some one is sink-ing to - day.

4

3 More than Conquerors.

J. E. RANKIN, D. D.　　　　　　　　　　　　　　　　W. A. OGDEN.

1. Thro' the cleansing blood of the dy-ing Lamb, Thro' the pow'r of grace
2. Who shall sev-er us from the Sav-ior's love, Or shall blot our names
3. More than con-quer-ors! There our Captain stands, While our names are grav-

and the precious name, Thro' the light that beams from the Morning Star,
from Life's book a-bove? Neither pres-ent things, nor the things to come,
en up-on His hands; Tho' the pow'rs of dark-ness a-gainst us frown,

Rit.　　REFRAIN.

More than con-querors, con-quer-ors we are.
Shall de-feat our souls of the heav'nly home.
We shall win the fight, and shall wear the crown.
} More than conquerors, more than

con-quer-ors, Thro' the cleans-ing blood of the dy-ing Lamb, More than

Rit.

conquerors! More than conquerors, Thro' the pow'r of grace and the precious name.

4   I Must Tell Jesus.

E. A. H.

Rev. Elisha A. Hoffman.

1. I must tell Je - sus all of my tri - als; I can-not bear these
2. I must tell Je - sus all of my troub-les; He is a kind, com-
3. Tempted and tried I need a great Sav - ior, One who can help my
4. O how the world to e - vil al-lures me! O how my heart is

burdens a - lone; In my distress he kind - ly will help me; He ev-er
passionate Friend; If I but ask him, he will de - liv - er, Make of my
burdens to bear; I must tell Je - sus, I must tell Je - sus; He all my
tempted to sin! I must tell Je - sus, and he will help me O - ver the

loves and cares for his own.
troub-les quick-ly an end.
cares and sor-rows will share.
world the vic - t'ry to win.

CHORUS.

I must tell Je - sus! I must tell Je - sus! I can-not bear my bur-dens a - lone; I must tell

Rit.

Je - sus! I must tell Je - sus! Je-sus can help me, Je-sus a - lone.

The Haven of Rest.

H. L. GILMOUR.

GEO. D. MOORE.

1. My soul in sad ex-ile was out on life's sea, So
2. I yield-ed my-self to his ten-der em-brace, And
3. The song of my soul, since the Lord made me whole, Has
4. How pre-cious the thought that we all may re-cline, Like
5. Oh, come to the Sav-ior, he pa-tient-ly waits To

:S:

burdened with sin and dis-trest, Till I heard a sweet voice say-ing,
faith tak-ing hold of the Word, My fet-ters fell off, and I
been the OLD STO-RY so blest, Of Je-sus, who'll save who-so-
John the be-lov-ed and blest, On Je-sus' strong arm, where no
save by his pow-er di-vine; Come, an-chor your soul in the

D. S.—The tem-pest may sweep o'er the

FINE.

"make me your choice;" And I en-tered the "Ha-ven of Rest!"
an-chored my soul; The "Ha-ven of Rest" is my Lord.
ev-er will have A home in the "Ha-ven of Rest!"
tem-pest can harm,— Se-cure in the "Ha-ven of Rest!"
"Ha-ven of Rest," And say, "my Be-lov-ed is mine."

wild, storm-y deep, In Je-sus I'm safe ev-er-more.

CHORUS.

D. S.

I've anchored my soul in the "Haven of Rest," I'll sail the wide seas no more;

Whiter than Snow.

E. R. LATTA.
Moderato.
H. S. PERKINS.

1. Bless-ed be the Fountain of blood, To a world of sin-ners revealed;
2. Thorny was the crown that he wore, And the cross his bod-y o'er-came;
3. Fa-ther, I have wandered from thee, Oft-en has my heart gone a-stray;

Bless-ed be the dear Son of God; On-ly by his stripes we are healed.
Grievous were the sorrows he bore, But he suffered thus not in vain.
Crim-son do my sins seem to me— Wa-ter can-not wash them a-way.

Tho' I've wandered far from his fold, Bringing to my heart pain and woe,
May I to that Fountain be led, Made to cleanse my sins here below;
Je-sus, to that Fountain of thine, Lean-ing on thy promise I go;

Wash me in the blood of the Lamb, And I shall be whit-er than snow.
Wash me in the blood that he shed, And I shall be whit-er than snow.
Cleanse me by thy washing di-vine, And I shall be whit-er than snow.

CHORUS.
Whit - - - - er than the snow, ... Whit - - - - er

Whiter than the snow, whiter than the snow, Whiter than the snow,

Whiter than Snow.

than the snow, ... Wash me in the Blood of the

whit-er than the snow; Wash me in the Blood of the

Lamb, ... And I shall be whit-er than snow.....

Lamb, of the Lamb, And I shall be whit-er than snow, than snow.

rit.

snow. ....

7 Jesus Will Let You In.

A. S. K.

A. S. KIEFFER.

1. { Come to the Fa-ther's house, Come ere the day be gone;
   { Tem-pests are gath-'ring fast, Dark-ness is com-ing on.

2. { Look at the wea-ry way, Look where thy feet have trod,
   { Find-ing no rest nor peace, Wan-d'ring a-way from God.

3. { Haste from the fields of sin, Fly for thy life to-day;
   { Come to our Fa-ther's house; En-ter the nar-row way.

CHORUS.

Fly, for the tem-pest is com-ing, Sweeping the fields of sin;

Knock at the por-tals of mer-cy, Je-sus will let you in.

Loyalty to Christ.

The tune on opposite page can be used if it is preferred.

LOU. P. BARRETT.

M. L. McPHAIL.

1. Our hearts have felt the rap-ture of the pres-ence of our God, We're
2. We've heard the call of Je-sus as it ech-oes thro' the soul, Louder
3. We've hosts of sin to con-quer in the name of Christ our King, We've
4. In "Loy-al-ty to Je-sus" we will ev-er do his will, The

press-ing on to vic-t'ry in the paths too long untrod, The cross of Christ our
than the call of trumpet or the solemn drum-beat's roll, The God who calls to
souls to win for Jesus till with joy the heav'ns shall ring, And Gospel words to
God that leads our forc-es will direct and bless us still; His ev-er-last-ing

sym-bol and sal-va-tion thro' his blood, Our hosts are marching on.
du-ty, of heart-serv-ice asks the whole, As he is marching on.
car-ry till the distant isles shall sing—That God is marching on.
prom-is-es he will in us ful-fill, As he is marching on.

CHORUS. m   f

Loy-al-ty to Christ as-sures us Vic-to-ry so grand and glo-rious;

ff   *Ritard.*

All our foes shall fall be-fore us, Our God is march-ing on.
march-ing on.

Our Youth are Marching On.

The tune on opposite page can be used if it is preferred.

Rev. Levi Gilbert, D. D.   Tune: Battle Hymn of the Republic.

1. Mine eyes have seen the to-kens of an-oth-er Pen-te-cost,
2. There's a fire of con-se-cra-tion that is kin-dling in our youth,
3. There's a fer-vor of re-vi-val burning bright in ma-ny hearts,
4. They un-furl Im-man-uel's ban-ner, and, be-hold, the thou-sands rise!

Mine ears have heard the gath-'ring of a ded-i-ca-ted host,
They are vow-ing heart-y serv-ice to the Mas-ter and his truth,
There's a glow of gen-'rous loy-al-ty their no-ble pur-pose starts,
They are look-ing up in pray'r to him enthroned be-yond the skies,

My soul has felt the pres-ence of the promised Ho-ly Ghost, Our
Their faith is pure and ar-dent, and their works are gos-pel proof, Our
'Tis the spir-it of the fa-thers and the zeal that Christ imparts, Our
They are lift-ing up their brother from the ru-in where he lies, Our

CHORUS.

youth are marching on. Look up, lift up, night is flee-ing! Look up, lift up,

day is breaking! Look up, lift up, vict'ry cometh! Our youth are marching on.

Entire Consecration.

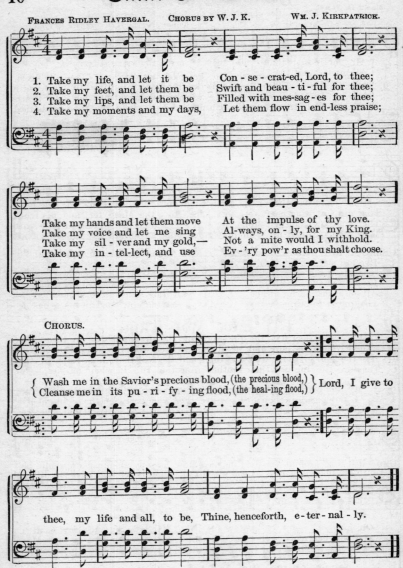

Frances Ridley Havergal.   Chorus by W. J. K.   Wm. J. Kirkpatrick.

1. Take my life, and let it be   Con - se - crat-ed, Lord, to thee;
2. Take my feet, and let them be   Swift and beau - ti - ful for thee;
3. Take my lips, and let them be   Filled with mes-sag - es for thee;
4. Take my moments and my days,   Let them flow in end-less praise;

Take my hands and let them move   At the impulse of thy love.
Take my voice and let me sing   Al-ways, on - ly, for my King.
Take my sil - ver and my gold,—   Not a mite would I withhold.
Take my in - tel-lect, and use   Ev - 'ry pow'r as thou shalt choose.

Chorus.

{ Wash me in the Savior's precious blood, (the precious blood,) } Lord, I give to
{ Cleanse me in its pu - ri - fy - ing flood, (the heal-ing flood,) }

thee, my life and all, to be, Thine, henceforth, e - ter - nal - ly.

5 Take my will, and make it thine;
It shall be no longer mine;
Take my heart,—it is thine own,—
It shall be thy royal throne.

6 Take my love,—my Lord, I pour
At thy feet its treasure-store!
Take myself, and I will be
Ever, only, all for thee!

11. All For Jesus.

MARY D. JAMES.
Arranged.

1. { All for Je-sus! all for Je-sus! All my being's ransomed pow'rs:
   { All my tho'ts, and words, and do-ings, All my days, and all my hours.

2. { Let my hands perform his bidding, Let my feet run in his ways—
   { Let my eyes see Je-sus on-ly, Let my lips speak forth his praise.

All for Jesus! all for Je-sus! All my days, and all my hours; hours.

All for Jesus! all for Je-sus! Let my lips speak forth his praise; praise.

3 Since my eyes were fixed on Jesus,
I've lost sight of all besides;
So enchained my spirit's vision,
Looking at the Crucified.
||: All for Jesus! all for Jesus!
Looking at the Crucified. :||

4 Oh, what wonder! how amazing!
Jesus, glorious King of kings—
Deigns to call me his beloved,
Lets me rest beneath his wings.
||: All for Jesus! all for Jesus!
Resting now beneath his wings. :||

12. I'll Live For Him.

C. R. DUNBAR.

1. My life, my love I give to thee, Thou Lamb of God, who died for me;
2. I now believe thou dost re-ceive, For thou hast died that I might live;
3. Oh, thou who died on Cal-va-ry, To save my soul and make me free,

CHO.—I'll live for him who died for me, How hap-py then my life shall be!

D. C.

Oh, may I ev-er faith-ful be, My Sav-ior and my God!
And now henceforth I'll trust in thee, My Sav-ior and my God!
I con-se-crate my life to thee, My Sav-ior and my God!

I'll live for him who died for me, My Sav-ior and my God!

13 The Best Friend Is Jesus.

P. B.

P. BILHORN.

DUET. Sop. (or Ten.) & Alto.

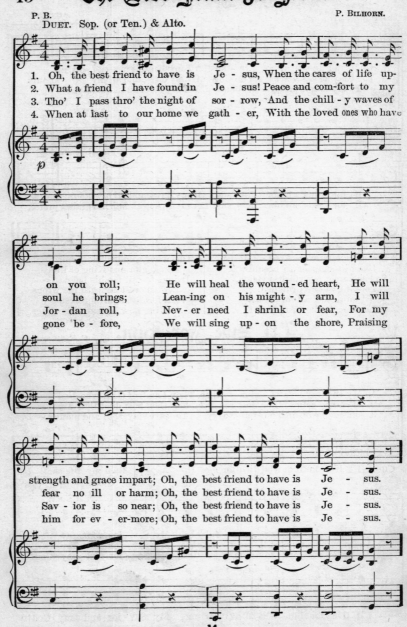

1. Oh, the best friend to have is Je - sus, When the cares of life up-
2. What a friend I have found in Je - sus! Peace and com-fort to my
3. Tho' I pass thro' the night of sor - row, And the chill - y waves of
4. When at last to our home we gath - er, With the loved ones who have

on you roll; He will heal the wound - ed heart, He will
soul he brings; Lean-ing on his might - y arm, I will
Jor - dan roll, Nev - er need I shrink or fear, For my
gone 'be - fore, We will sing up - on the shore, Praising

strength and grace impart; Oh, the best friend to have is Je - sus.
fear no ill or harm; Oh, the best friend to have is Je - sus.
Sav - ior is so near; Oh, the best friend to have is Je - sus.
him for ev - er-more; Oh, the best friend to have is Je - sus.

The Best Friend Is Jesus.

CHORUS. *Spirited.*

The best friend to have is Je - - - sus, The best friend to have is
Je-sus ev-'ry day,

Je - - - sus, He will help you when you fall, He will
Je - sus all the way;

hear you when you call; Oh, the best friend to have is Je - sus.

14

Jesus, Savior, Pilot Me.

J. E. GOULD.

Rev. EDWARD HOPPER.

FINE.

1. Je - sus, Sav - ior, pi - lot me, O - ver life's tempestuous sea;
D.C. Chart and compass came from thee; Je - sus, Sav - ior, pi - lot me.
2. As a moth - er stills her child, Thou canst hush the o - cean wild;
D.C. Wondrous Sovereign of the sea, Je - sus, Sav - ior, pi - lot me.
3. When at last I near the shore, And the fear - ful breakers roar,
D.C. May I hear thee say to me, "Fear not, I will pi - lot thee!"

D. C.

Unknown waves before me roll, Hid-ing rocks and treacherous shoal;
Boisterous waves o-bey thy will When thou say'st to them, "Be still!"
'Twixt me and the peaceful rest, Then while leaning on thy breast,

15 The Very Same Jesus.

L. H. EDMUNDS.

WM. J. KIRKPATRICK.

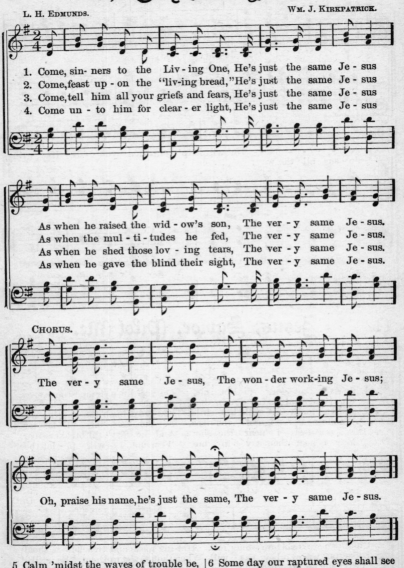

1. Come, sin-ners to the Liv-ing One, He's just the same Je-sus
2. Come, feast up-on the "liv-ing bread," He's just the same Je-sus
3. Come, tell him all your griefs and fears, He's just the same Je-sus
4. Come un-to him for clear-er light, He's just the same Je-sus

As when he raised the wid-ow's son, The ver-y same Je-sus.
As when the mul-ti-tudes he fed, The ver-y same Je-sus.
As when he shed those lov-ing tears, The ver-y same Je-sus.
As when he gave the blind their sight, The ver-y same Je-sus.

CHORUS.

The ver-y same Je-sus, The won-der work-ing Je-sus;

Oh, praise his name, he's just the same, The ver-y same Je-sus.

5 Calm 'midst the waves of trouble be,
   He's just the same Jesus
   As when he hushed the raging sea,
   The very same Jesus.

6 Some day our raptured eyes shall see
   He's just the same Jesus;
   Oh, blessed day for you and me!
   The very same Jesus.

16 I Am Coming to the Cross.

Rev. Wm. McDonald.   Wm. G. Fischer.

1. I am com - ing to the Cross; I am poor, and weak, and blind;
2. Long my heart has sighed for thee, Long has e - vil reigned with-in;
3. Here I give my all to thee, Friends, and time, and earth - ly store;

CHO.—I am trust-ing, Lord, in thee, Blest Lamb of Cal - va - ry;

D. C.

I am count-ing all but dross, I shall full sal - va - tion find.
Je - sus sweet - ly speaks to me,—"I will cleanse you from all sin."
Soul and bod - y thine to be,—Whol - ly thine for ev - er - more.

Humbly at thy Cross I bow, Save me, Je - sus, save me now.

4 In thy promises I trust,
    Now I feel the blood applied:
I am prostrate in the dust,
    I with Christ am crucified.

5 Jesus comes! he fills my soul!
    Perfected in him I am;
I am every whit made whole:
    Glory, glory to the Lamb.

17 He Is Calling.

F. W. Faber.   Arr. by S. J. Vail.

1. { There's a wideness in God's mercy, Like the wideness of the sea:
     There's a kindness in his justice Which is more than [Omit.] lib-er-ty,
2. { There is welcome for the sinner, And more graces for the good;
     There is mer-cy with the Savior, There is heal-ing [Omit.] in his blood.

CHORUS.

He is call-ing, "Come to me!" Lord, I glad - ly haste to thee.

3 For the love of God is broader
    Than the measure of man's mind;
And the heart of the Eternal
    Is most wonderfully kind.

4 If our love were but more simple,
    We should take him at his word;
And our lives would be all sunshine
    In the sweetness of our Lord.

18. Light is Shining.

I. N. McH.   I. N. McHose.

1. Are you liv - ing in the darkness? Light is shin-ing on be - fore;
2. Are there doubts and fears within you, Clouds of darkness hov-'ring o'er?
3. Are the shades of death ap-pear-ing? Do not fear the Jor-dan's roar;
4. Walk no long - er in the dark-ness; Give your fears and doubtings o'er;

Christ, the Sun, in all his brightness, Glows with beauty more and more.
Look to Christ, and find in look-ing, Light is shin-ing more and more.
Christ and home and friends are nearing In the light from Heaven's shore.
Trust in God, and go right onward Where the light shines more and more.

CHORUS.

Light is shin-ing more and more, Shining clearer on be-fore, Clear and
clearer, bright and brighter on be-fore, Shining clearer on before, Shining
brighter on before, Light is shining, light is shin-ing more and more.

19. Where He Leads I'll Follow.

W. A. O.

W. A. OGDEN.

1. Sweet are the prom-is-es, Kind is the word, Dear-er far than
2. Sweet is the ten-der love Je - sus hath shown, Sweeter far than
3. List to his lov-ing words, "Come un - to me," Wea-ry, heav-y

an - y mes-sage man ev-er heard; Pure was the mind of Christ,
an - y love that mortals have known; Kind to the err - ing one,
lad-en, there is sweet rest for thee; Trust in his prom - is - es,

Sin-less I see; He the great ex - am - ple is, and pattern for me.
Faith-ful is he; He the great ex - am - ple is, and pattern for me.
Faith-ful and sure; Lean up - on the Sav - ior, and thy soul is se-cure.

CHORUS.

Where . . . . he leads I'll fol - - - - low,
Where he leads I'll fol - low, Where he leads I'll fol - low,

1. Fol - - - - low all the way, 2. Follow Jesus ev'ry day.
Follow all the way, yes, follow all the way.

Love Found Me.

H. L. GILMOUR.

Arr. by H. L. G.

1. When out in sin and dark-ness lost, Love found me, My
2. The Spir - it roused me from my sleep, Love found me, Con-
3. I'll praise him while he gives me breath, Love found me, For
4. And when I reach the gold-paved street, Love found me, I'll

faint - ing soul was tem - pest tossed, Love found me; I
vic - tion seized me strong and deep, Love found me; Al-
sav - ing from an end - less death, Love found me; Christ
sit a - dor - ing at his feet, Love found me, And

heard the Savior's words so blest, Love found me, "Come, wea - ry, heav - y-
though I long withstood his grace, Love found me, He wooed me to his
is my ad - vo - cate a - bove, Love found me, I'm yoked to him in
sing ho - san - nas round the throne, Love found me, Where I shall know as

CHORUS.

la - den, rest," Love found me. Oh, 'twas love, love,
kind em - brace, Love found me.
per - fect love, Love found me.
I am known, Love found me. Oh, 'twas love, 'twas won-drous love,

Love that moved the mighty God, Love, love, 'twas love found me.

21 Beautiful, Beckoning Hands.

C. C. L.

May be sung as a Solo or Duet with Chorus.

C. C. LUTHER.

1. Beck-on-ing hands at the gate-way to-night, Fa-ces a-
2. Beck-on-ing hands of a moth-er whose love Sac-ri-ficed
3. Beck-on-ing hands of a lit-tle one, see! Ba-by voice
4. Beck-on-ing hands of a hus-band, a wife, Watch-ing and
5. Bright-est and best of that glo-ri-ous throng, Cen-ter of

shin-ing with ra-di-ant light; Eyes look-ing down from yon
life its de-vo-tion to prove; Hands of a fa-ther to
call-ing, O moth-er, for thee; Ro-sy-cheek'd dar-ling, the
wait-ing the loved one of life; Hands of a broth-er, a
all and the theme of their song, Je-sus our Sav-ior, the

heav-en-ly home, Beau-ti-ful hands, they are beck-on-ing "come."
mem-o-ry dear, Beck-on up high-er the wait-ing ones here.
light of the home, Ta-ken so ear-ly, is beck-on-ing "come."
sis-ter, a friend, Out from the gate-way to-night they ex-tend.
pierc-ed One stands, Lov-ing-ly call-ing with beck-on-ing hands.

REFRAIN.

Beau-ti-ful hands, beckoning hands, Call-ing the dear ones to heaven-ly lands;

Beau-ti-ful hands, beckoning hands, Beau-tiful, beau-tiful, beckon-ing hands.

22 Wandering Away.

E. R. LATTA.   KNOWLES SHAW.

1. Wan-der - er a-way from Je-sus,   In the wind-ing ways of   sin,
2. Wan-der - er a-way from Je-sus,   In the road to end-less woe,
3. Wan-der - er a-way from Je-sus, Wouldst thou not a crown ob - tain?

Turn and seek the world's Redeemer, And his serv-ice now be - gin.
If thou wilt not turn to Je - sus, Whither, whith-er wilt thou go?
Why then wilt thou slight his goodness? Fear-est not the woe and pain?

On Mount Cal-va - ry he suffered, On the cru - el cross he died;
Broad the road where thou art go-ing, Ma - ny with thee downward move;
Can you bar - ter life e - ter-nal, For the pleasure sin can give?

See his hands and feet so wounded, And be-hold his pierc-ed side.
Turn and seek the nar-row pathway, That will lead to bliss a - bove.
Turn, oh, turn you to the Sav-ior, And a fade-less crown re - ceive.

CHORUS.

Wandering a-way, wandering a-way, Wandering a-way from Je-sus;

Wandering Away.

Hear his gentle voice, Calling you to-day, And wander no more away from Jesus.

23

Bring Them In.

ALEXCENAH THOMAS.   W. A. OGDEN.

1. Hark! 'tis the Shepherd's voice I hear,   Out in the des-ert dark and drear,
2. Who'll go and help this Shepherd kind, Help him the wand'ring ones to find?
3. Out in the des-ert hear their cry,   Out on the mountain wild and high,

Call-ing the sheep who've gone astray,   Far from the Shepherd's fold a-way.
Who'll bring the lost ones to the fold,   Where they'll be shelter'd from the cold?
Hark! 'tis the Mas-ter speaks to thee,   "Go, find my sheep where'er they be."

CHORUS.

Bring them in,   Bring them in,   Bring them in from the fields of sin;

Bring them in,   Bring them in,   Bring the wand'ring ones to Je-sus.

24 Pass It On.

Rev. Henry Burton, A. M.

Wm. J. Kirkpatrick.

1. Have you had a kind-ness shown? Pass it on, Pass it on! 'Twas not
2. Did you hear the lov-ing word! Pass it on, Pass it on! Like the
3. Have you found the heav'n-ly light? Pass it on, Pass it on! Souls are

given for thee a-lone, Pass it on, pass it on! Let it trav-el down the
sing-ing of a bird? Pass it on, pass it on! Let its mu-sic live and
grop-ing in the night, Day-light gone, day-light gone! Hold your lighted lamp on

years, Let it wipe an-oth-er's tears; Till in heav'n the deed ap-pears,
grow, Let it cheer an-oth-er's woe; You have reaped what others sow,
high, Be a star in some one's sky, He may live who else would die,

D. S. Christ, you live a-gain, Live for him, with him you reign,

FINE. CHORUS.

Pass it on, pass it on! Pass it on, (pass it on,) pass it on! (pass it on!) Cheerful

D. S.

word or loving deed, Pass it on, (pass it on,) Live for self, you live in vain; Live for

24

25 The Fullness of Blessing.

Chorus by E A. H.
Arranged.

1. Ho-ly Spir-it, dwell with me, Make me ho-ly, like to thee;
2. Lov-ing Spir-it, come to me, Make me lov-ing, like to thee;
3. Might-y Spir-it, live in me, I would heav'nly-mind-ed be;
4. Glorious Spir-it, fill thou me! This poor heart I yield to thee;

Bring thou ev-'ry tho't of mine In-to har-mo-ny with thine;
To its depths my be-ing stir, Print my Mas-ter's likeness there;
Let my heart its Sovereign own, Christ its cen-ter—Christ a-lone;
Take me bod-y, spir-it, soul, Let thy life per-vade the whole;

Bring thou ev-'ry tho't of mine In-to har-mo-ny with thine.
To its depths my be-ing stir, Print my Mas-ter's likeness there.
Let my heart its Sovereign own, Christ its cen-ter—Christ a-lone.
Take me bod-y, spir-it, soul, Let thy life per-vade the whole.

CHORUS.

Fill thou me! fill thou me! All my heart I yield to thee!

With thy ho-li-ness di-vine Fill this long-ing heart of mine!

Never to Say Farewell.

Rev. ELISHA A. HOFFMAN.

IRA ORWIG HOFFMAN.

Unison.*

1. { We journey to the home a-bove, Never to say farewell,
   { To yon fair pal-a-ces of love, ... Nev-er to say fare-

2. { We'll meet our sainted parents there, Never to say farewell,
   { And heav'n with sisters, brothers, share, ... Nev-er to say fare-

Harmony.

Unison. Rit.

well; Within that glorious summer land The many jewel'd mansions stand, And
well; Upon the plains of perfect light, Upon the pavements golden bright, We'll

Harmony. CHORUS.

there we'll meet, at God's right hand, Never to say farewell. Never to say farewell,
walk with them, enrob'd in white, Never to say farewell.

Never to say farewell, O we shall meet at God's right hand, Never to say farewell.

3 We'll meet beyond life's swelling flood,
　　Never to say farewell,
Redeemed and washed in Jesus' blood,
　　Never to say farewell;
Earth's long, long night will pass away,
Dissolving into heavenly day,
And we shall with our loved ones stay,
　　Never to say farewell.

4 O what a blessed hope is this,
　　Never to say farewell!
What pure and perfect happiness,
　　Never to say farewell!
Delivered from all sin and pain,
To reach yon fair, celestial plain,
And meet the loved and lost again,
　　Never to say farewell.

*Very effective if unison parts are sung as a solo.

27 Standing on the Promises.

R. K. C.   R. Kelso Carter.

1. Stand-ing on the prom-is-es of Christ my King, Thro' e - ter - nal
2. Stand-ing on the prom-is-es that can not fail, When the howl - ing
3. Stand-ing on the prom-is-es I now can see Per - fect, pres - ent
4. Stand-ing on the prom-is-es of Christ the Lord, Bound to him e -
5. Stand-ing on the prom-is-es I can not fall, List'ning ev - 'ry

a - ges let his prais-es ring; Glo-ry in the high-est, I will shout and sing,
storms of doubt and fear as-sail, By the living Word of God I shall pre - vail,
cleansing in the blood for me; Standing in the lib - er-ty where Christ makes free,
ter - nal-ly by love's strong cord, Overcoming dai - ly with the Spirit's sword,
moment to the Spir-it's call, Resting in my Sav - ior, as my all in all,

CHORUS.

Standing on the promises of God. Stand - ing, Stand - ing,
Standing on the promise, Standing on the promise,

Stand - - ing,

Standing on the prom-is-es of God my Sav - ior; Standing on the promise,

Stand - - - ing,

Stand-ing on the promise, I'm stand-ing on the promis-es of God.

Who'll Be the Next?

ELLA LAUDER.

D. B. TOWNER.

1. Who'll be the next to fol-low Je-sus, Tread-ing the bright and
2. Who'll be the next to bow be-fore him? Who'll be the next his
3. Who'll be the next to reach the kingdom, Leav-ing be-hind, the
4. Who'll be the next to heed the summons, "Come un-to me, Oh,

heav'n-ly way Lead-ing from earth to realms of glo-ry,
praise to sing, And with the host of saints a-dore him,
path of sin, Look-ing to Je-sus for sal-va-tion,
wea-ry one?" Do not neg-lect the in-vi-ta-tion,

CHORUS.

Lead-ing from night to end-less day? Who'll be the next,
Reign-ing a-bove, our Lord and King?
Bear-ing the cross the crown to win?
You may not see to-mor-row's sun. Oh,

Who'll be the next, Who'll be the next the yoke to wear? Who'll be the
Oh,

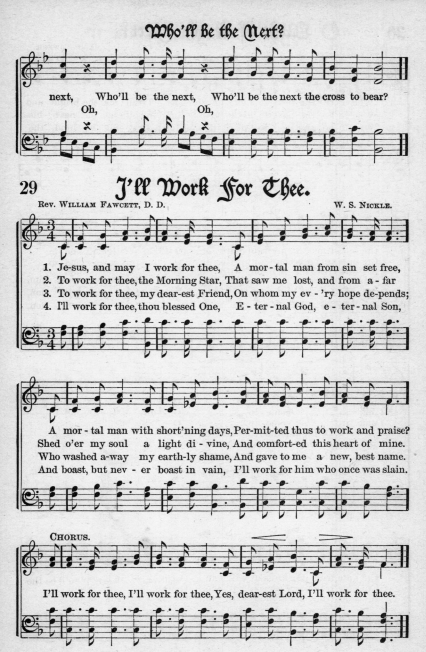

Who'll Be the Next?

next, Who'll be the next, Who'll be the next the cross to bear?

Oh,   Oh,

29. I'll Work For Thee.

Rev. WILLIAM FAWCETT, D. D.   W. S. NICKLE.

1. Je-sus, and may I work for thee, A mor-tal man from sin set free,
2. To work for thee, the Morning Star, That saw me lost, and from a-far
3. To work for thee, my dear-est Friend, On whom my ev-'ry hope de-pends;
4. I'll work for thee, thou blessed One, E-ter-nal God, e-ter-nal Son,

A mor-tal man with short'ning days, Per-mit-ted thus to work and praise?
Shed o'er my soul a light di-vine, And comfort-ed this heart of mine.
Who washed a-way my earth-ly shame, And gave to me a new, best name.
And boast, but nev-er boast in vain, I'll work for him who once was slain.

CHORUS.

I'll work for thee, I'll work for thee, Yes, dear-est Lord, I'll work for thee.

30 O Light of Light, Shine in.

HORATIUS BONAR. Alt.

W. A. OGDEN.

1. O Light of light, shine in, shine in; Cast out this night of gloom and sin;
2. O Joy of joys, come in, come in, And end this night of grief and sin;
3. O Life of life, come in, come in, Ex - pel this night of death and sin;

Cre - ate true day my soul with - in, O Light of light, shine in.
Cre - ate true peace my soul with - in, O Joy of joys, come in.
A - wake true life my soul with - in, O Life of life, come in.

REFRAIN.

Shine in,...... shine in,........ O Light di-vine, shine in;
Come in,...... come in,........ O Joy of joys, come in;
Come in,...... come in,........ O Life of life, come in;

O Light shine in, shine in,
O Joy of joys, come in,
O Life of life, come in,

Cre - ate true day my soul with - in, O Light of light, shine in.
Cre - ate true peace my soul with - in, O Joy of joys, come in.
A - wake true life my soul with - in, O Life of life, come in.

31 Sunshine in the Soul.

E. E. HEWITT.   JNO. R. SWENEY.

1. There's sunshine in my soul to-day, More glo - ri - ous and bright
2. There's mu - sic in my soul to-day, A car - ol to my King,
3. There's spring-time in my soul to-day, For when the Lord is near,
4. There's glad-ness in my soul to-day, And hope, and praise, and love,

Than glows in an - y earth - ly sky, For Je - sus is my light.
And Je - sus, list - en - ing, can hear The songs I can - not sing.
The dove of peace sings in my heart, The flowers of grace ap - pear.
For bless-ings which he gives me now, For joys "laid up" a - bove.

REFRAIN.

Oh, there's sun - - - - shine, Bless-ed sun - - - shine,
sun-shine in the soul, sun-shine in the soul,

While the peace - ful, hap-py mo-ments roll;
hap-py moments roll; When

Je - sus shows his smil-ing face, There is sunshine in the soul.

32 The World Must Be Taken.

LANTA WILSON SMITH.

G. TABOR THOMPSON.

1. The world must be tak-en for the Lord; Onward, sol-diers, and
2. The world must be tak-en for the Lord; And if faith-ful we
3. The world must be tak-en for the Lord; Fi-nal vic-t'ry is
4. The world must be tak-en for the Lord; Ev-'ry na-tion and

arm ye for the fight; "In His name" now watch and fight and pray, Till all
know that we shall win. Each day there's a shout a-long the line As we
near-er ev-'ry day. The past holds no rec-ord of a time When so
land shall yet be won. His ban-ner shall wave o'er all the world, For our

CHORUS.

foes fear and trem-ble at the sight. Ev-er on - - - ward,
cap-ture some cit-a-del of sin.
ma-ny as now the Lord o-bey.
God with his ar-my marches on. Ev-er onward, ev-er onward,

Chris-tian sol - - - dier, The world must be tak-en for the
Chris-tian sol-dier, Christian sol-dier, The world must be tak-en for the

Lord, Ev-er on - - - ward be your
Lord, for the Lord, Ev-er on-ward, ev-er on-ward be your

The World must be Taken.

watch - - - word, The world must be taken for the Lord.
watchword, be your watchword, The world must be taken for the Lord, for the Lord.

He Calleth Thee.

33

JESSIE L. SPORE.

W. A. OGDEN.

1. Hark, I hear the Sav - ior call-ing, "All ye wea - ry, come to me!
2. "I will make thy bur-den light-er, I will give thee rest from pain,
3. Heed the voice that gen-tly calls thee, Heed be-fore it is too late;

To that fount-ain flow-ing free-ly—Flow-ing free-ly now for thee."
I will make thy path-way brighter, Sin shall smite thee ne'er a-gain."
Or at last when death shall claim thee, Thou shalt stand outside the gate.

f CHORUS.

m

"Come to me, and I will save thee;" List to Je-sus' gen-tle call;

f

p

"I will par-don, cleanse, redeem thee;" Hear the lov-ing mes-sage fall.

34 Wondrously Redeemed.

E. A. H.

Rev. Elisha A. Hoffman.

1. I have pre - cious news to tell, hal - le - lu - jah! Christ has
2. It was Christ's re - demp - tion - blood, hal - le - lu - jah! That re -
3. I have found a pre - cious friend, hal - le - lu - jah! On whose

come with me to dwell, halle - lu - jah! By his grace and pow'r di - vine, He has
stored my soul to God, halle - lu - jah! He the cleansing stream applied, Flowing
help I can depend, halle - lu - jah! Since he took my sins a - way, He has

D. S. joic - ing night and day, As I

FINE.

changed this heart of mine, And he whispers, "I am thine," hal - le - lu - jah!
from his wounded side; I am saved and jus - ti - fied, hal - le - lu - jah!
taught me how to pray, And to do his will each day, hal - le - lu - jah!

walk the nar - row way, For he washed my sins a - way, hal - le - lu - jah!

CHORUS.

Hal - le - lu - - - - - - jah! I'm re - deemed! Oh, so

Hal - le - lu - jah! I'm redeem'd! oh, hal - le - lu - jah! I'm redeem'd! Oh, so

won - - - - - drous-ly re - deemed! D. S.

won-drous-ly redeemed, yes, oh, so won-drous-ly redeemed! I'm re-

35 Where the Shepherd Leads.

A. P. COBB.

J. H. FILLMORE.

1. Thro' the meadows green, in-vit-ing, Where the Shepherd leads I'll go,
2. See the gen-tle Shep-herd lead-ing! Where the Shepherd leads I'll go;
3. Tho' my feet be worn and wea-ry, Where the Shepherd leads I'll go;

Thro' the shad-ows dark, ex-cit-ing, Where the Shepherd leads I'll go.
Hark, his voice in mer-cy plead-ing! Where the Shepherd leads I'll go.
Tho' the mountain-side be drear-y, Where the Shepherd leads I'll go.

CHORUS.

Hark! his voice is gen-tly call-ing, On my ear its

strains are fall-ing; Though the gloom may be ap-pall-ing,

Where the Shepherd leads I'll go, I'll go, Where the Shepherd leads I'll go.

36 Onward, Christian Workers.

Rev. Levi Gilbert, D. D.   Chas. H. Gabriel.

1. For-ward, Christian workers, Quit yourselves like men, Wielding gos-pel
2. Might-y re-in-force-ments Thrill the church with cheer; Freshly press the
3. Trust-ing in his prowess, Home and na-tion rest; Fu-ture a-ges
4. Rout and pan-ic seize them, All the hosts of wrong; Soon for you the

weapons, Force the fight a-gain; Yours are strength and dar-ing,
vet-'rans, Not a sign of fear; Thinned by age and death-stroke,
sig-nal Each to do his best; Hast-en earth's re-demp-tion,
conquest, Soon the vic-tor's song; What are toils or dan-gers,

Con-fi-dent and free; Rouse to splendid ac-tion, Fer-vid loy-al-ty!
Ranks fill up with youth; Sons in fathers' plac-es, Stand defending truth!
Bring the per-fect law; Speed millennial glo-ries, Visions prophets saw.
Marches, wounds or pain? Christ is near his triumph, You with him shall reign.

CHORUS.

On-ward, Chris-tian work-ers, Raise your bat-tle cry;

Look-ing up to Je-sus, Lift your stand-ard high.

36

37 We'll Endeavor.

F. M. D.

FRANK M. DAVIS.

1. By the help of God, we'll en-deav - or To gath - er the lost ones
2. By the help of God, we'll en-deav - or To spread the glad news a -
3. By the help of God, we'll en-deav - or In Christ's work to nev - er

in, Who have strayed a - way on the mount - ains, Who
broad, Of the Christ who saves and re - deems men, Who
pause, Give our means and time with our tal - ents, To

CHORUS.

dwell in the haunts of sin.
calls wand'rers home to God. } We'll en - deav - or, we'll en -
help on our Mas - ter's cause.

deav - or, By the help of God we'll en - deav - or; To the

fold of Christ from the haunts of sin, We will gath-er the lost ones in.

38 Walk In the Light.

Words arranged.   Arr. by F. A. Scott.

1. 'Tis re - lig - ion that can give, In the light, in the light,
2. 'Tis Christ Je - sus must sup - ply, In the light, in the light,
3. Aft - er death our joys will be, In the light, in the light,
4. Be the liv - ing God my Friend, In the light, in the light,

Sweet-est pleas - ure while we live, In the light of God.
Sol - id com - fort when we die, In the light of God.
Last - ing as e - ter - ni - ty, In the light of God.
Then my bliss shall nev - er end, In the light of God.

CHORUS.

Let us walk in the light, In the
Let us walk in the light,

light.........in the light, Let us walk in the
Let us walk in the light of God; Let us walk

light, In the light,........ the light of God.
in the light, Let us walk in the light of God.

39 Let Him In.

Rev. J. B. Atchinson.

E. O. Excell.

1. There's a stran-ger at the door, Let him in,
2. O - pen now to him your heart, Let him in,
3. Hear you now his lov - ing voice, Let him in,
4. Now ad - mit the heav'nly Guest, Let him in,
Let the Savior in, Let the Savior in,

He has been there oft be - fore, Let him in;
If you wait he will de - part, Let him in;
Now, oh, now make him your choice, Let him in;
He will make for you a feast, Let him in;
Let the Savior in, Let the Savior in,

Let him in ere he is gone, Let him in, the Ho - ly One,
Let him in, he is your Friend, He your soul will sure de - fend,
He is stand-ing at the door, Joy to you he will re - store,
He will speak your sins for-given, And when earth ties all are riven,

Je- sus Christ, the Fa-ther's Son, Let him in.
He will keep you to the end, Let him in.
And his name you will a - dore, Let him in.
He will take you home to heaven, Let him in.
Let the Savior in, Let the Savior in.

40 Leaning on the Everlasting Arms.

Rev. E. A. HOFFMAN.   A. J. SHOWALTER.

1. What a fel-lowship, what a joy divine, Lean-ing on the ev-er-
2. Oh, how sweet to walk in this pilgrim way, Lean-ing on the ev-er-
3. What have I to dread, what have I to fear, Lean-ing on the ev-er-

last-ing arms; What a bless-ed-ness, what a peace is mine,
last-ing arms; Oh, how bright the path grows from day to day,
last-ing arms? I have bless-ed peace with my Lord so near,

REFRAIN.

Lean-ing on the ev-er-last-ing arms. Lean - ing,
Lean-ing on the ev-er-last-ing arms.
Lean-ing on the ev-er-last-ing arms. Lean - ing on Je - sus,

lean - ing, Safe and se-cure from all a-larms;
Lean - ing on Je - sus,

Lean - ing, lean - ing, Lean-ing on the ev-er-last-ing arms.
Leaning on Je-sus, leaning on Je-sus,

41 Glory To His Name.

Rev. E. A. Hoffman.   Rev. J. H. Stockton.

1. Down at the cross where my Sav-ior died, Down where for cleansing from
2. I am so won-drous-ly sav'd from sin, Je - sus so sweetly a-
3. Oh, precious fountain, that saves from sin, I am so glad I have
4. Come to this fountain, so rich and sweet; Cast thy poor soul at the

sin I cried; There to my heart was the blood applied; Glo-ry to his
bides within; There at the cross where he took me in; Glo-ry to his
en-tered in; There Je-sus saves me and keeps me clean, Glo-ry to his
Sav-ior's feet; Plunge in to-day, and be made complete; Glo-ry to his

D. S.—There to my heart was the blood applied; Glo-ry to his

Fine. Chorus.   D.S.

name.   Glo-ry to his name,   Glo-ry to his name;

42 Happy Day.

P. Doddridge.   ENGLISH MELODY.

1. { O hap-py day, that fixed my choice On thee, my Sav-ior and my God!
     Well may this glowing heart rejoice, And tell its raptures all a-broad. }

Fine.   D.S.

Happy day, happy day, When Jesus washed my sins away! { He taught me how to watch and pray,
                                                          And live rejoicing ev'ry day. }

2 'Tis done! the great transaction's done!
  I am my Lord's, and he is mine:
  He drew me, and I followed on,
    Charmed to confess that voice divine.

3 Now rest, my long-divided heart;
  Fixed on this blissful center, rest;

Nor ever from thy Lord depart;
  With him of every good possessed.

4 High heav'n that heard the solemn vow,
    That vow renewed shall daily hear,
  Till in life's latest hour I bow,
    And bless in death a bond so dear

41

43 The Bird with a Broken Wing.

HEZEKIAH BUTTERWORTH.

J. H. TENNEY.

mp Effective as a Solo.

1. I walked in the woodland meadows, Where sweet the thrushes sing,
2. I found a young life bro-ken By sin's se-duc-tive art,
3. But the bird with a bro-ken pin-ion, Kept an-oth-er from the snare,

And found on a bed of moss-es, A bird with a bro-ken wing.
And touched with a Christ-like pit-y, I took him to my heart;
And the life that sin had stricken, Raised an-oth-er from de-spair;

I healed its wing, and each morning It sang its old sweet strain,
He lived with a no-bler pur-pose, And struggled not in vain,
Each loss has its own com-pen-sa-tion, There's healing for each pain,

But the bird with the bro-ken pin-ion, Nev-er soared as high a-gain;
But the life that sin had strick-en, Nev-er soared as high a-gain;
But the bird with the bro-ken pin-ion, Nev-er soared as high a-gain;

But the bird with the bro-ken pin-ion, Nev-er soared as high a-gain.
But the life that sin had strick-en, Nev-er soared as high a-gain.
But the bird with the bro-ken pin-ion, Nev-er soared as high a-gain.

42

44 What A Wonderful Savior!

E. A. H.

ELISHA A. HOFFMAN.

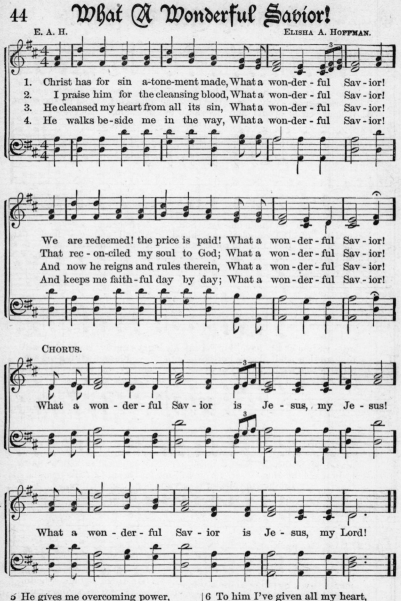

1. Christ has for sin a-tone-ment made, What a won-der-ful Sav-ior!
2. I praise him for the cleansing blood, What a won-der-ful Sav-ior!
3. He cleansed my heart from all its sin, What a won-der-ful Sav-ior!
4. He walks be-side me in the way, What a won-der-ful Sav-ior!

We are redeemed! the price is paid! What a won-der-ful Sav-ior!
That rec-on-ciled my soul to God; What a won-der-ful Sav-ior!
And now he reigns and rules therein, What a won-der-ful Sav-ior!
And keeps me faith-ful day by day; What a won-der-ful Sav-ior!

CHORUS.

What a won-der-ful Sav-ior is Je-sus, my Je-sus!

What a won-der-ful Sav-ior is Je-sus, my Lord!

5 He gives me overcoming power,
    What a wonderful Savior!
And triumph in each conflict hour,
    What a wonderful Savior!

6 To him I've given all my heart,
    What a wonderful Savior!
The world shall never share a part,
    What a wonderful Savior!

43

45 Abundantly Able To Save.

E. A. HOFFMAN.

P. P. BLISS.

1. Who-ev-er re-ceiv-eth the Cru-ci-fied One, Who-ev-er be-
2. Who-ev-er re-ceiv-eth the mes-sage of God, And trusts in the
3. Who-ev-er re-pents and for-sakes ev-'ry sin, And o-pens his

liev - eth on God's on - ly Son, A free and a per-fect
pow'r of the soul-cleansing blood, A full and e-ter-nal
heart for the Lord to come in, A pres-ent and per-fect

sal - va-tion shall have, For he is a-bund-ant-ly a-ble to save.
re-demption shall have, For he is both a-ble and willing to save.
sal - va-tion shall have, For Jesus is read-y this moment to save.

CHORUS.

My brother! the Mas - - ter is call-ing for thee; . . . . His grace and his
Brother, the Master is come and is calling for thee,

mer - - cy are wondrously free; . . . . His blood as a ran - - som
Brother, his grace and his mercy are wondrously free,
Brother, his blood as

Abundantly Able to Save.

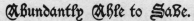

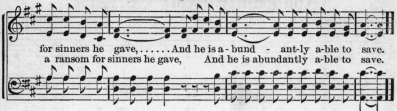

for sinners he gave,......And he is a - bund - ant-ly a-ble to save.
a ransom for sinners he gave, And he is abundantly a-ble to save.

46

The Gospel Feast.

CHARLES WESLEY.
Cho. by H. L. G.

H. L. GILMOUR.

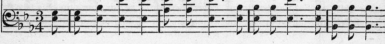

1. Come, sinners, to the gos-pel feast; It is for you, it is for me;
2. Ye need not one be left be-hind, It is for you, it is for me;

:S:

FINE.

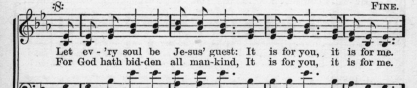

Let ev - 'ry soul be Je-sus' guest: It is for you, it is for me.
For God hath bid-den all man-kind, It is for you, it is for me.

D. S.—O wea - ry wand'rer come and see, It is for you, it is for me.

CHORUS.

D. S.

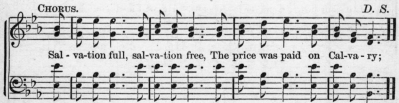

Sal - va-tion full, sal-va-tion free, The price was paid on Cal-va-ry;

3 Sent by my Lord, on you I call;
The invitation is to all:

4 Come, all the world! come, sinner, thou!
All things in Christ are ready now.

5 Come, all ye souls by sin oppressed,
Ye restless wanderers after rest;

6 Ye poor and maimed and halt and blind
In Christ a hearty welcome find.

7 My message as from God receive;
Ye all may come to Christ and live:

8 O let this love your hearts constrain,
Nor suffer him to die in vain.

9 See him set forth before your eyes,
That precious, bleeding sacrifice:

10 His offered benefits embrace,
And freely now be saved by grace.

47 Lift your Heart in Prayer.

G. T. T.

G. Tabor Thompson.

1. Lift your heart in prayer to Je - sus, He is full of truth and grace;
2. Lift your heart in prayer to Je - sus, He can ev'ry need sup-ply;
3. Lift your heart in prayer to Je - sus, When you prosper in the way;
4. Lift your heart in prayer to Je - sus, When in sorrow's darkest hour,

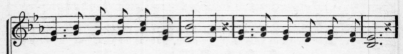

All of light and all of knowledge Shin-eth ev - er in his face.
Tell him all your care and troub-le, None like him can sat - is - fy.
For the tempter seeks to snare you, Tho' all seems as bright as day.
He will know just how to rest you, Praise his name, he has the power.

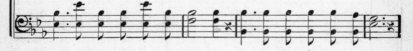

CHORUS.

Lift your heart in prayer to Je - sus, He will lead you all the way;

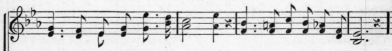

Lift your heart in prayer to Je - sus, With - out ceasing ev-'ry day.

48 Fill Me Now.

Rev. E. H. STOKES, D. D.
JNO. R. SWENEY.

1. Hov-er o'er me, Ho-ly Spir-it; Bathe my trembling heart and brow;
2. Thou canst fill me, gracious Spir-it, Tho' I can not tell thee how;
3. I am weakness, full of weakness; At thy sa-cred feet I bow;
4. Cleanse and comfort; bless and save me; Bathe, oh, bathe my heart and brow;

Fill me with thy hal-low'd presence, Come, oh, come and fill me now.
But I need thee, great-ly need thee, Come, oh, come and fill me now.
Blest di-vine, e-ter-nal Spir-it, Fill with power, and fill me now.
Thou art com-fort-ing and sav-ing, Thou art sweet-ly fill-ing now.

D.S. Fill me with thy hallow'd presence;—Come, oh, come and fill me now.

CHORUS.   D. S.

Fill me now, fill me now, Je-sus, come and fill me now;

49 Come, Holy Spirit.

ISAAC WATTS.
Tune: ORTONVILLE. C. M.

1 Come, Holy Spirit, heavenly Dove,
  With all thy quick'ning powers;
  Kindle a flame of sacred love
  In these cold hearts of ours.

2 Father, and shall we ever live
  At this poor dying rate—
  Our love so faint, so cold to thee
  And thine to us so great?

3 Come, Holy Spirit, heavenly Dove,
  With all thy quick'ning powers;
  Come, shed abroad a Savior's love,
  And that shall kindle ours.

50

1 Jesus, my life, thyself apply,
  Thy Holy Spirit breathe:
  My vile affections crucify;
  Conform me to thy death.

2 Reign in me, Lord; thy foes control,
  Who would not own thy sway;
  Diffuse thine image through my soul;
  Shine to thy perfect day.

3 Scatter the last remains of sin,
  And seal me thine abode;
  O make me glorious all within,
  A temple built by God!

CHARLES WESLEY.

51 Not Far From the Kingdom.

E. R. LATTA.

J. H. TENNEY.

1. Not far from the kingdom of heav-en,—The kingdom of heaven with men,
2. Not far from the kingdom of heav-en,—The kingdom of peace and of love,
3. Not far from the kingdom of heav-en, Yet will not on Je - sus be-lieve!

And yet in the bondage of Sa - tan, And yet in the shad-ow of sin!
Yet out on the edge of the des - ert, The prod - i - gal's for-tune to prove!
O sin - ner, what terrors a-wait thee! The blessing of par - don re-ceive!

Not far from the path that is nar-row, And lead-eth to glo - ry on high;
Oh, rise, and re-turn to thy Fa - ther, And crave in his mer - cy a share!
The por - tal of mer - cy is o - pen, Poor prod - i - gal, do not de - lay!

Yet treading the broad road to ru - in,—Oh, why is it, sin-ner? oh why?
Far off he will see thee and know thee, And res-cue thy soul from despair!
A - rise, and re-turn to thy Fa - ther! Oh, en - ter the kingdom to-day!

CHORUS.

Not far, not far, Not far from the kingdom of heaven!
Not far, not far, the kingdom of heaven!

Not Far From the Kingdom.

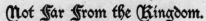

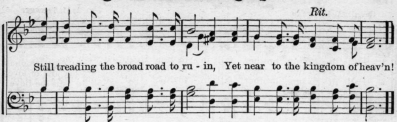

Still treading the broad road to ru - in, Yet near to the kingdom of heav'n!

52   Heaven Is Not Far Away.

C. E. L.   C. E. LESLIE.

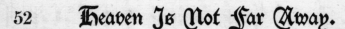

1. Heav-en is not far a-way, When Je-sus is near; Give your heart to
2. Will you not re-pent, believe, When Je-sus is near? Peace and par-don
3. Are you coming home to-day, When Je-sus is near? Do not long-er

him I pray, When Je-sus is near. Place your trust in him, dear friend,
now receive, When Je-sus is near. He will not your pray'r refuse,
stay a-way, When Je-sus is near. Cast your burdens on the Lord,

He will keep you to the end, Heaven is not far away, When Jesus is near.
Come and now the Savior choose, Heaven is not far away, When Jesus is near.
He has promised in his word, Heaven is not far away, When Jesus is near.

53   Fall Into Line.

Rev. E. A. Hoffman.
J. H. Tenney.

1. Fall in-to line,*brother, fall in-to line! Heark-en with me, to the
2. Fall in-to line, brother, fall in-to line! See how the hosts of the
3. Fall in-to line, brother, fall in-to line! God is om-nip-o-tent

mes-sage di-vine! Je-sus in-vites you to join in the fray,
foe-man com-bine! Join in the con-flict and rush to the field,
and he shall win! On-ly be true to thy-self and the Lord,

CHORUS.

Gives you as-sur-ance of vic-t'ry to-day. Fall   in-to
Till we shall crush and com-pel them to yield.
And you shall share the e-ter-nal reward. Fall in-to line,

line,   sol-diers, fall   in-to line,
fall in-to line;   Fall in-to line, sol-diers, fall in-to line!

On   to the bat - tle, for Je-sus shall win! Fierce is the war
On to the battle, fall in-to line! Je-sus shall win!

Fall into Line.

Rit.

fare with Sa-tan to-day; Arm for the con-flict, and march to the fray.

54 Onward, Christian Soldiers!

SABINE BARING-GOULD.   Tune, "Onward." 6, 5.

1. On-ward, Christian sol-diers! Marching as to war, With the cross of
2. Like a might-y ar - my Moves the Church of God; Brothers, we are
3. Crowns and thrones may per-ish, Kingdoms rise and wane, But the Church of
4. Onward, then, ye peo-ple! Join our hap-py throng, Blend with ours your

Je - sus Go - ing on be - fore, Christ, the roy - al Mas - ter,
tread-ing Where the saints have trod; We are not di - vid - ed,
Je - sus Con-stant will re - main; Gates of hell can nev - er
voic - es In the tri-umph song; Glo - ry, laud, and hon - or

Leads a-gainst the foe; Forward in - to bat-tle, See, his ban-ners go!
All one bod - y we, One in hope and doctrine, One in char - i - ty.
'Gainst that Church prevail, We have Christ's own promise, And that cannot fail.
Un - to Christ the King, This thro' countless a-ges Men and an-gels sing.

CHORUS.

Onward, Christian soldiers! Marching as to war, With the cross of Jesus Going on be - fore.

Able to Deliver.

W. A. O.

W. A. OGDEN.

1. "He is a-ble to de-liv-er," Sing the joyful strain, "He is a-ble to de-
2. He is a-ble to de-liv-er From the chains of sin, He is a-ble to de-
3. He is a-ble to de-liv-er From the foe-man strong, He is a-ble to de-

liv-er," Tell it out a-gain, "He is a-ble to de-liv-er" All that
liv-er, Shout the joy-ful strain, He is a-ble to de-liv-er, See how
liv-er, All the jour-ney long, He is a-ble to de-liv-er, Trust him

come to him in faith, He is a-ble to de-liv-er E-ven
pa-tient-ly he stands, He is a-ble to de-liv-er Thee with
bold-ly, nev-er fear, He is a-ble to de-liv-er; Let the

CHORUS.

un-to death. A - - ble to de-liv-er,
will-ing hands.
na-tions hear. A-ble to de-liv-er, He is a-ble to de-liv-er,

A - - ble to de-liv-er,   He is
A-ble to de-liv-er, He is a-ble to de-liv-er,

Able to Deliver.

a - - ble to de-liv-er,   All that come to him in faith.

A-ble to de-liv-er, He is a - ble to de-liv-er

56   Believe and be Saved.

Miss ADA BLENKHORN.   PETER BILHORN.

1. The voice of thy conscience oft whispers, Believe on the Lord and be saved,
2. A voice in com-pas-sion is cry-ing, Believe on the Lord and be saved,
3. God's voice and his goodness are call-ing, Believe on the Lord and be saved,
4. The voice of the Spir-it is plead-ing, Believe on the Lord and be saved,

And turn from the path of transgressors; Believe on the Lord and be saved.
And cease from your sor-row and sigh-ing; Believe on the Lord and be saved.
The judg-ment of death is ap-pall-ing; Believe on the Lord and be saved.
While loved ones are now in-ter-ced-ing, Believe on the Lord and be saved.

Be sav'd,.... be sav'd,.... Believe on the Lord and be saved, Be
be sav'd,   be sav'd,

Rit.

sav'd,.... be sav'd,.... Believe on the Lord and be sav'd.....
be sav'd,   be sav'd,   be sav'd.

Jesus Lives!

Rev. John. R. Colgan.

A. F. Myers.

1. Might-y ar-my of the young, Lift the voice in cheer-ful song,
2. Tongues of children light and free, Tongues of youth all full of glee,
3. Je-sus lives, oh, bless-ed words! King of kings, and Lord of lords!

Send the welcome word a-long, Jesus lives! Once he died for you and me,
Sing to all on land and sea, Jesus lives! Light for you and all mankind,
Lift the cross and sheathe the swords, Jesus lives! See, he breaks the prison wall,

Bore our sins up-on the tree, Now he lives to make us free, Jesus lives!
Sight for all by sin made blind, Life in Jesus all may find, Jesus lives!
Throws a-side the dread-ful pall, Conquers death at once for all, Jesus lives!

CHORUS.

Wait not till the shadows lengthen, till you older grow, Rally now and
Wait not,   Sing,

Wait not, wait not,   Sing for

sing for Je-sus, ev-'ry-where you go, Lift your joy-ful voic-es high,
sing,

Je - sus,

Jesus Lives!

Repeat Chorus pp.
f Rit.

Ringing clear thro' earth and sky, Let the blessed tidings fly, *Jesus lives!*

58

Crown Him To-day.

Mrs. E. C. Ellsworth.   J. H. Tenney.

1. Come, look on the King in his beau-ty, And gaze on his reconciled face;
2. Come, look on the King in his beau-ty, Oh, look, and thy heart shall be won;
3. Come, look on the King in his beau-ty, And o - pen thy lips in his praise;

Enthroned in thy heart he ap-pear-eth, Adorned with an in - fi - nite grace.
His love shall come out in its sweetness, And Je - sus will claim thee his own.
Oh, sing till the world shall be hearing The anthem thy spir - it shall raise.

CHORUS.

Enthrone him thy King and thy Sav-ior, His loving commands to o - bey;

Oh, give to the King all his glo-ry, And crown him to - day.
And crown him, yes crown him to-day.

59 When the Roll is Called up Yonder.

B. M. J.

J. M. BLACK.

1. When the trum-pet of the Lord shall sound, and time shall be no
2. On that bright and cloudless morning when the dead in Christ shall
3. Let us la-bor for the Mas-ter from the dawn till set-ting

more, And the morning breaks, e-ter-nal, bright and fair; When the
rise, And the glo-ry of his res-ur-rec-tion share; When his
sun, Let us talk of all his wondrous love and care, Then when

saved of earth shall gath-er o-ver on the oth-er shore, And the
chos-en ones shall gath-er to their home be-yond the skies, And the
all of life is o-ver and our work on earth is done, And the

CHORUS.

roll is called up yon-der, I'll be there. When the roll........ is
roll is called up yon-der, I'll be there.
roll is called up yon-der, I'll be there. When the roll is

called up yon - - der, When the roll........ is called up
called up yon-der, I'll be there, When the roll is called up

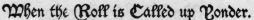

When the Roll is Called up Yonder.

yon - - der, When the roll.......... is called up
yon - der, I'll be there, When the roll is called up

yon - der, When the roll is called up yon - der, I'll be there.

60 Bringing in the Sheaves.

KNOWLES SHAW.

GEO. A. MINOR.

CHORUS.

FINE.

After repeat D. S. to Fine.

1 Sowing in the morning, sowing seeds of kindness,
  Sowing in the noontide, and the dewy eves;
  Waiting for the harvest, and the time of reaping,
  We shall come rejoicing, bringing in the sheaves.

CHO. Bringing in the sheaves, bringing in the sheaves,
  We shall come rejoicing, bringing in the sheaves.

2 Sowing in the sunshine, sowing in the shadows,
  Fearing neither clouds nor winter's chilling breeze;
  By and by the harvest, and the labor ended,
  We shall come rejoicing, bringing in the sheaves.

3 Go then, ever weeping, sowing for the Master,
  Though the loss sustained our spirit often grieves;
  When our weeping's over, he will bid us welcome,
  We shall come rejoicing, bringing in the sheaves.

61 No Other Grace.

ELISHA A. HOFFMAN.

W. A. OGDEN.

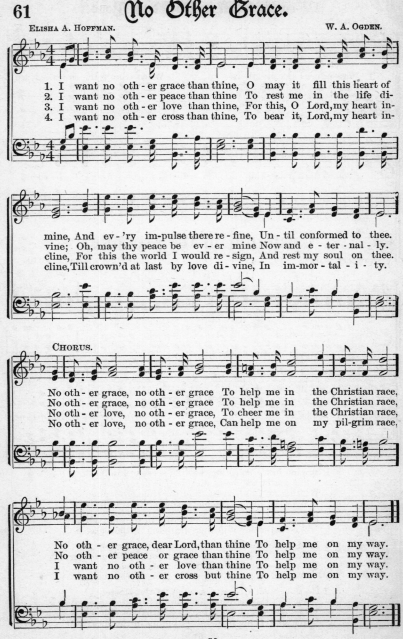

1. I want no oth-er grace than thine, O may it fill this heart of
2. I want no oth-er peace than thine To rest me in the life di-
3. I want no oth-er love than thine, For this, O Lord, my heart in-
4. I want no oth-er cross than thine, To bear it, Lord, my heart in-

mine, And ev-'ry im-pulse there re-fine, Un-til conformed to thee.
vine; Oh, may thy peace be ev-er mine Now and e-ter-nal-ly.
cline, For this the world I would re-sign, And rest my soul on thee.
cline, Till crown'd at last by love di-vine, In im-mor-tal-i-ty.

CHORUS.

No oth-er grace, no oth-er grace To help me in the Christian race,
No oth-er grace, no oth-er grace To help me in the Christian race,
No oth-er love, no oth-er grace, To cheer me in the Christian race,
No oth-er love, no oth-er grace, Can help me on my pil-grim race,

No oth-er grace, dear Lord, than thine To help me on my way.
No oth-er peace or grace than thine To help me on my way.
I want no oth-er love than thine To help me on my way.
I want no oth-er cross but thine To help me on my way.

62 Blessed Assurance.

F. J. CROSBY.

Mrs. JOS. F. KNAPP.

1. Bless-ed as - sur-ance, Je - sus is mine! Oh, what a fore-taste of
2. Per - fect sub-mis-sion, per-fect de - light, Vis - ions of rap - ture now
3. Per - fect sub-mis-sion, all is at rest, I in my Sav - ior am

glo-ry di - vine! Heir of sal - va-tion, pur-chase of God, Born of his
burst on my sight, An-gels de-scend-ing, bring from a - bove Ech-oes of
hap-py and blest, Watching and waiting, look-ing a - bove, Filled with his

CHORUS.

Spir - it, washed in his blood.
mer - cy, whis-pers of love. } This is my sto - ry, this is my
good-ness, lost in his love.

song, Prais-ing my Sav - ior all the day long; This is my

sto - ry, this is my song, Praising my Sav-ior all the day long.

63 Story of the Cross.

Rev. W. P. Rivers.   R. M. McIntosh.

1. Oh, the gos-pel sto-ry tell Of the cross! (of the cross!) Let the
2. Let us plead the ho-ly name Of the cross! (of the cross!) And the
3. Oh, the song shall nev-er cease Of the cross! (of the cross!) Of the

ech-o rise and swell Of the cross! (of the cross!) Sing the
Savior's pain and shame Of the cross! (of the cross!) For his
mercy, grace and peace, Of the cross! (of the cross!) For its

Sav-ior's grief and woe, How his blood did free-ly flow, Till the
name must be our plea, For sal-va-tion full and free, And in
glo-ry gilds the way, And it hath im-mor-tal ray, And we'll

D. S. blood did free-ly flow, Till the

FINE. CHORUS.

chil-dren all shall know Of the cross! Of the cross,..... of the
death our hope must be Of the cross!
sing in heav'n for aye Of the cross!

Of the cross on which the

chil-dren all shall know Of the cross!

D. S.

cross!............... Sing the Sav-ior's grief and woe, How his
bless-ed Sav-ior died,

Anywhere With Jesus.

JESSIE H. BROWN.   D. B. TOWNER.

1. An - y-where with Je-sus I can safe-ly go, An - y-where he
2. An - y-where with Je-sus I am not a - lone, Oth - er friends may
3. An - y-where with Je-sus I can go to sleep, When the dark - ning

leads me in this world be - low; An - y-where with-out him, dear-est
fail me, he is still my own; Tho' his hand may lead me o - ver
shad-ows round a - bout me creep; Knowing I shall wak-en nev - er

joys would fade, An - y-where with Je - sus I am not a - fraid.
drear-est ways, An - y-where with Je - sus is a house of praise.
more to roam, An - y-where with Je - sus will be home, sweet home.

CHORUS.

An - y-where! an - y-where! Fear I can not know,

An - y-where with Je - sus I can safe - ly go.

65 Through the Blood of Jesus.

Mrs. Harriet Jones.　　　　　　　　　　A. J. Abbey.　Arr. by J. H. T.

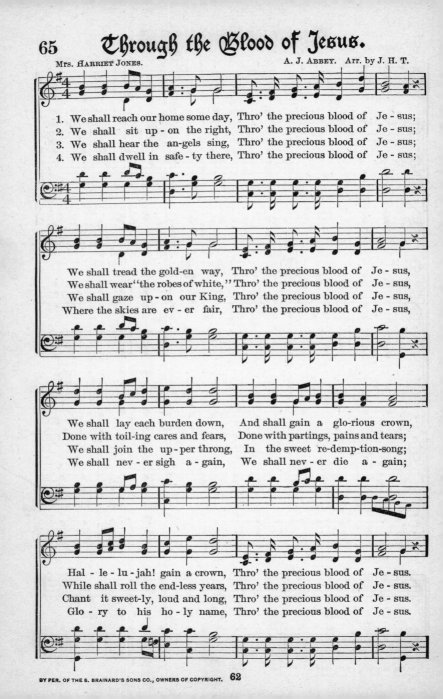

1. We shall reach our home some day, Thro' the precious blood of Je-sus;
2. We shall sit up-on the right, Thro' the precious blood of Je-sus;
3. We shall hear the an-gels sing, Thro' the precious blood of Je-sus;
4. We shall dwell in safe-ty there, Thro' the precious blood of Je-sus;

We shall tread the gold-en way, Thro' the precious blood of Je-sus,
We shall wear "the robes of white," Thro' the precious blood of Je-sus,
We shall gaze up-on our King, Thro' the precious blood of Je-sus,
Where the skies are ev-er fair, Thro' the precious blood of Je-sus,

We shall lay each burden down, And shall gain a glo-rious crown,
Done with toil-ing cares and fears, Done with partings, pains and tears;
We shall join the up-per throng, In the sweet re-demp-tion-song;
We shall nev-er sigh a-gain, We shall nev-er die a-gain;

Hal - le - lu - jah! gain a crown, Thro' the precious blood of Je - sus.
While shall roll the end-less years, Thro' the precious blood of Je - sus.
Chant it sweet-ly, loud and long, Thro' the precious blood of Je - sus.
Glo - ry to his ho - ly name, Thro' the precious blood of Je - sus.

62

Through the Blood of Jesus.

CHORUS.

Precious blood! crimson flood! Oh, the precious blood of Je-sus! Hal - le -
lu - jah, we shall gain a glorious crown, Thro' the precious blood of Jesus!

66

Pass Me Not.

FANNY J. CROSBY.   W. H. DOANE.

1. Pass me not, O gen - tle Sav - ior,   Hear my hum - ble cry;
2. Let me, at thy throne of mer - cy,   Find a sweet re - lief;
3. Trust - ing on - ly in thy mer - its,   Would I seek thy face;
4. Thou, the spring of all my com - fort,   More than life to me—

:S: FINE.

While on oth-ers thou art smil - ing,   Do not pass me by.
Kneel - ing there in deep con-tri - tion,   Help my un - be - lief.
Heal my wounded, broken spir - it,   Save me by thy grace.
Whom have I on earth be-side thee?   Whom in heav'n but thee?

D. S.—While on oth-ers thou art call - ing,   Do not pass me by.

REFRAIN.   *D. S.*

Sav - ior, Sav - ior, Hear my hum - ble cry;

67 Jesus Is Calling.

Fanny J. Crosby.   Geo. C. Stebbins.

1. Je - sus is ten - der - ly call - ing thee home,— Call - ing to - day,
2. Je - sus is call - ing the wea - ry to rest,— Call - ing to - day,
3. Je - sus is wait - ing, oh, come to him now,— Wait - ing to - day,
4. Je - sus is plead - ing, oh, list to his voice,— Plead - ing to - day,

call - ing to - day; Why from the sun - shine of love wilt thou roam,
call - ing to - day; Bring him thy bur - den and thou shalt be blest:
wait - ing to - day; Come with thy sins, at his feet low - ly bow,
plead - ing to - day; They who be - lieve on his name shall re - joice;

CHORUS.

Far - ther and far - ther a - way?   Call - - ing to - day, . . .
He will not turn thee a - way.
Come, and no long - er de - lay.
Quick - ly a - rise and a - way.   Call - ing, call - ing to - day, to - day,

call - - ing to - day; . . . . .   Je - - - - sus is
call - ing, call - ing to - day, to - day;   Je - sus is ten - der - ly

call - - - - ing, is ten - der - ly call - ing to - day.
call - ing to - day,

68 At the Cross.

Isaac Watts.   R. E. Hudson.

1. A - las! and did my Sav - ior bleed, And did my Sovereign die,
2. Was it for crimes that I had done, He groan'd up-on the tree?
3. But drops of grief can ne'er re-pay, The debt of love I owe;

Would he de-vote that sa-cred head For such a worm as I?
A - maz - ing pit - y, grace unknown, And love be-yond de-gree!
Here, Lord, I give my-self a - way, 'Tis all that I can do!

CHORUS.

At the cross, at the cross, where I first saw the light, And the

bur - den of my heart roll'd a - way— It was there by faith

I re-ceived my sight, And now I am hap-py all the day.

COPYRIGHT, 1885, BY R. E. HUDSON.

69 Oh, How I Love Jesus!

John Newton.

[Omit in Repeat. . . . . .]

CHORUS.

[Omit in Repeat. . . . . .]

1 How sweet the name of Jesus sounds
In a believer's ear!
It soothes his sorrows, heals his wounds,
And drives away his fear.

CHO.—‖: Oh, how I love Jesus! :‖
Because he first loved me;
‖: How can I forget thee? :‖
Dear Lord, remember me.

2 It makes the wounded spirit whole,
And calms the troubled breast;
'Tis manna to the hungry soul,
And to the weary rest.

3 I would thy boundless love proclaim
With every fleeting breath;
So shall the music of thy name
Refresh my soul in death.

Keep a Light in the Window.

Mrs. E. C. Ellsworth.

J. H. Tenney.

1. Keep a light in the win-dow, my broth-er, The storm fierce-ly
2. Keep a light in the win-dow, my broth-er, Perchance there is
3. Keep a light in the win-dow, my broth-er, Il - lu-mined the

rag - es with-out, And winds in their fu - ry are blind-ing, The
some one a - stray; Just a gleam may give hope to the wea - ry, And
pathway should be; Keep a bright shining light in the win - dow, And

CHORUS.

trav - 'lers are grop-ing in doubt.
guide till the breaking of day.
night will be bright-er for thee.

Keep a light in the win-dow, my

broth-er, The temp - ter is set-ting a snare, But a ray from a

light in your win - dow May help the poor sin-ner be - ware.

Keep the Banner Flying.

Rev. Richard Osborne.   Robert Lowry.

1. Keep the banner flying! This your cry should be;   Ma - ny souls are dy-ing,
2. Keep the banner flying! When the faithful fall, Give not up to sighing,
3. Keep the banner flying! Christians should a - gree, With each oth - er vy-ing,
4. Keep the banner flying   O - ver land and sea;   By yourself de-ny-ing

Je - sus must they see.   Un - der condem-nation, Life will soon be gone;
Christ is All in all.   Ral - ly all your forces; See, the Captain's near;
Yet in har-mo-ny;   Working still for Je-sus, Righting human wrong,
Comes the vic - to - ry.   Bright-en toil with singing, Better days will come;

CHORUS.

On - ly is sal-va - tion In the sin - less One.
Trust to his re-sourc-es, There is naught to fear.
Till the angels greet us With their welcome song.   } Shout, shout the battle cry,
To the Savior clinging, You shall rest at home.

Girt with endeavor; Lift, lift the banner high, Now and for-ev- er. Shout, shout the

Rit.

bat-tle cry, Girt with endeavor; Lift, lift the banner high, Now and for-ev- er.

72 How Far to the City of Gold?

Mrs. E. E. Miles. Arr. by F. A. B.

F. A. Blackmer.

1. "How far, how far to the Cit - y of Gold?"........The anx-ious pilgrim
2. "How far, how far to the Cit - y of Gold?"........The sadden'd hearts would
3. "How far, how far to the Cit - y of Gold?"........Where sorrow ne'er shall
How far, how far?

cries, "How far to jour-ney ere I see Its towers be - fore me rise?"
know, While mourning o'er the friends they love, In death's embrace laid low;
come, The promised land of joy and rest, The saints' e - ter-nal home?

Tho' oft - en worn and sad, Oppressed with grief and care,
How long ere saints a - wake And pass those por - tals fair?
The jour-ney long has been, But home will soon ap - pear;

Pil-grim, press on a few more steps, Thy feet are al - most there.
Hope whis-pers in af - flic-tion's hour, Weep not, they're almost there.
Each land-mark past proclaims to us We're al - most, al - most there.

Chorus.

Press on,...... press on,......Where lies thy home so fair;...
Press on, press on, press on, press on, so fair;

How Far to the City of Gold?

Pilgrim, press on a few more steps, Thy feet are al-most, there.
almost there.

73   Oh, 'Tis Wonderful.

I. I. LESLIE.   F. A. BLACKMER.

1. When I was far a-way and lost, Oh, 'tis won-der-ful!
2. I once was blind, but now I see; Oh, 'tis won-der-ful!
3. My guilt was all I had to bring; Oh, 'tis won-der-ful!
4. Come, sin-ner, now, and seek his grace, Oh, 'tis won-der-ful!

That I was saved at such a cost! Oh, 'tis won-der-ful!
Was bound by sin, but now am free; Oh, 'tis won-der-ful!
Yet I was made his love to sing; Oh, 'tis won-der-ful!
And find in him a rest-ing place; Oh, 'tis won-der-ful!

CHORUS.

Oh, 'tis won-der-ful! Oh, .. 'tis won-der-ful,

That Je-sus gave his life for me! Oh, 'tis won-der-ful!

74 Jesus Is Passing By.

E. E. HEWITT.   JNO. R. SWENEY.

1. Come, con-trite one, and seek his grace, Je-sus is pass-ing by;
2. Come, hun-gry one, and tell your needs, Je-sus is pass-ing by;
3. Come, wea-ry one, and find your rest, Je-sus is pass-ing by;
4. Come, burden'd one, bring all your care, Je-sus is pass-ing by;

See in his rec-on-cil-ing face, The sun-shine of the sky.
The Bread of Life your soul will feed, And ful-ly sat-is-fy....
Come where the longing heart is bless'd, And on his bo-som lie...
The love that list-ens to your pray'r, Will "no good thing" de-ny.

CHORUS.

Pass - - ing by,...... pass - - ing by,......
mf Pass-ing by, pass-ing by, pass-ing by, pass-ing by.

Hast-en to meet him on the way, Je-sus is pass-ing

by to-day, Pass - - ing by,...... pass - - ing by......
Pass-ing by, pass-ing by, pass-ing by, pass-ing by.

75 My Jesus, I Love Thee.

London Hymn Book.

A. J. GORDON.

1. My Jesus, I love thee, I know thou art mine, For thee all the
2. I love thee, be-cause thou hast first lov-ed me, And purchased my
3. I will love thee in life, I will love thee in death, And praise thee as
4. In mansions of glo-ry and end-less de-light, I'll ev-er a-

fol-lies of sin I re-sign; My gra-cious Re-deem-er, my
par-don on Cal-va-ry's tree; I love thee for wear-ing the
long as thou lend-est me breath; And say when the death-dew lies
dore thee in heav-en so bright; I'll sing with the glit-ter-ing

Sav-ior art thou,
thorns on thy brow;
cold on my brow,
crown on my brow;
} If ev-er I loved thee, my Je-sus, 'tis now.

BY PERMISSION.

76 Come, Ye Disconsolate.

T. MOORE.

11, 10.

1. Come, ye dis-con-so-late, where'er ye languish, Come to the mercy-seat, fervently kneel;

Here bring your wounded hearts, here tell your anguish; Earth has no sorrow that Heav'n can not heal.

2 Joy of the desolate, light of the straying,
Hope of the penitent, fadeless and pure,
Here speaks the Comforter, tenderly saying,
"Earth has no sorrow that Heaven can not cure."

3 Here see the bread of life; see waters flowing
Forth from the throne of God, pure from above;
Come to the feast of love, come, ever knowing
Earth has no sorrow but Heaven can remove.

77 The Wondrous News.

F. M. D.

FRANK M. DAVIS.

1. Wondrous news! we'll raise the song   As   we   journey 'mid the throng,
2. Wondrous news! we'll raise the song, And the notes we will pro-long,
3. Wondrous news! we'll raise the song   As we join the ransomed throng,

Of   a   Sav-ior's gra-cious love to - day; How on Calvary's rugged mount
Of the Christ that saves from ev-'ry sin; Who - so-ev - er will be-lieve,
Marching homeward to the land on high; There our loved ones gone before,

He has   o-pened up   a fount That will wash the stains of sin a - way.
Peace and par-don shall re-ceive, And the blest assurance know with-in.
Wait for us up-on the shore; Thro' his love we'll meet them by and by.

CHORUS.

We will tell   We will tell
the wondrous news,   the gra-cious news,

Of   a Sav-ior's dy - ing love to - day; We will tell,
the wondrous news,

We will tell the gracious news, Of a Savior's precious love to-day.

78. Why Stand Ye Idle?

E. A. H.

Rev. E. A. HOFFMAN.

1. Why stand ye i-dle, wait-ing, While Christ is call-ing you?
2. The fields are white and rip-ened; The har-vest time is here;
3. Some hearts are touched with sorrow, And some are touched with sin;
4. Some homes with gloom are shad-ed; Some lives are cheer-less, sad;
5. And some poor souls, dis-cour-aged With fail-ure and with sin,

For in his world-wide vine-yard There's work for all to do.
The Mas-ter pleads for toil-ers; His call—can you not hear?
Poor wan-der-ers from Je-sus, Oh! haste to bring them in.
Go bear to them the mes-sage That Christ can make them glad.
At Mer-cy's door are wait-ing For us to lead them in.

CHORUS.

Why i-dle? why wait-ing To ren-der serv-ice true?
Why i-dle stand? why waiting stand?

Oh! ev-'ry-where we turn us There's earn-est work to do.

79 My old Country Home. *

G. Tabor Thompson.　　　　　　　　　　　　　　　J. H. Tenney.

1. In thought I trav - el back to-night To my old coun-try home;
2. I left my room and gen-tly crept Down to the o - pen door,
3. The Ho - ly Book was o-pened then, And moth - er read a - loud
4. A ho - ly hush came o'er my soul, As on their knees they fell;
5. I gave my heart to God that night, Ere they rose up from prayer;

What joy-ful scenes flash thro' my mind As in the past I roam!
And heard my moth-er join the song, And chant it o'er and o'er;
A - bout the home pre-pared on high, A - bove the storm and cloud;
They prayed as tho' they were inspired; So list - en while I tell;
Then saw them kiss each oth-er's face, Tho' fur-rowed deep with care;

My moth-er with her locks of snow, Is knit - ting in her chair,
Since then in cit - ies, great and small, I've heard the cul-tured sing,
That hum-ble cot - tage seemed to me Grand as the man-sions fair,
They prayed for pas - tor, neighbor, friend, And then they prayed for me:
A - gain I heard a sweet re-frain While I stole back to rest;

While fa-ther, sit-ting by her side, Sings this fa - mil-iar air:
But no such rapture to my heart Could all their mu - sic bring.
And I am sure be - fore they knelt, The an - gels hov-ered there.
"O Je-sus, grant that our dear boy May fol - low on - ly thee."
Help me to sing it o'er a-gain, In mem - 'ry of the blest.

My old Country Home.

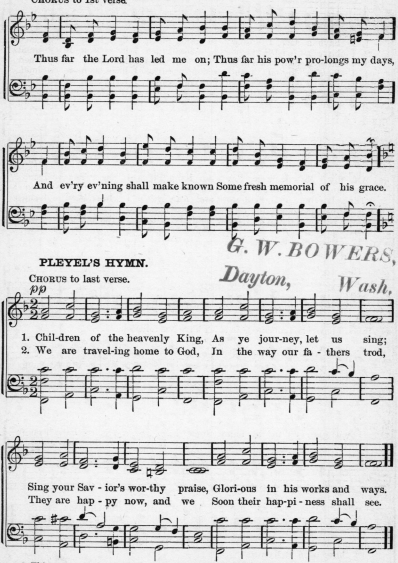

HEBRON.

Chorus to 1st verse.

Thus far the Lord has led me on; Thus far his pow'r pro-longs my days,

And ev'ry ev'ning shall make known Some fresh memorial of his grace.

G. W. BOWERS, Dayton, Wash.

PLEYEL'S HYMN.

Chorus to last verse.

pp

1. Chil-dren of the heavenly King, As ye jour-ney, let us sing;
2. We are trav-el-ing home to God, In the way our fa-thers trod,

Sing your Sav-ior's wor-thy praise, Glori-ous in his works and ways.
They are hap-py now, and we Soon their hap-pi-ness shall see.

✱ This song may be used as a solo, the choir or congregation singing the familiar tunes at the close of the first and last verses. It may also be sung as a quartet, and may be made very effective by having the familiar tunes sung by voices in an adjoining room. The chorus to the last verse should be sung very softly.

80 Since I Have Been Redeemed.

E. O. E.

E. O. EXCELL.

1. I have a song I love to sing, Since I have been re-deemed,
2. I have a Christ that sat-is-fies, Since I have been re-deemed,
3. I have a Wit-ness bright and clear, Since I have been re-deemed,
4. I have a joy I can't ex-press, Since I have been re-deemed,
5. I have a home pre-pared for me, Since I have been re-deemed,

Of my Re-deem-er, Sav-ior King, Since I have been re-deemed.
To do his will my high-est prize, Since I have been re-deemed.
Dis-pell-ing ev-'ry doubt and fear, Since I have been re-deemed.
All thro' his blood and right-eous-ness, Since I have been re-deemed.
Where I shall dwell e-ter-nal-ly, Since I have been re-deemed.

CHORUS.

Since I.......have been re-deemed, Since I have been redeemed,
Since I have been redeemed, since I have been redeemed,

I will glo-ry in his name, Since I..........have been re-
Since I have been re-deemed, since

deemed, I will glo-ry in the Sav-ior's name.
I have been redeemed,

81 Come to the Living Water.

JENNIE WILSON.   W. A. OGDEN.

1. Hark! the Sav-ior speaks with gen-tle voice To each heart with guilt op-
2. Who-so-ev-er will, may come and drink Of this liv-ing wa-ter
3. O-ver des-ert sands, in paths of sin, Stray no more with wea-ry

prest, Here is liv-ing wa-ter, soul athirst, Come drink, and be at rest.
free; Thirsty one, where life's pure fountain flows, There is a gift for thee.
feet; The re-fresh-ing stream in-vit-eth thee To joy and rest complete.

CHORUS.

The Spir-it and the Bride say come,........ Oh,
come, oh, come,

come, and no more de-lay; Life's wa-ter is free, Christ

call-eth thee, Sin-la-den soul, oh, come to-day.

Sowing, Ever Sowing.

E. R. LATTA.

J. M. HOGAN.
Arr. by D. E. DORTCH.

1. We are sow - ing, ev-er sowing, In the paths where others move,
2. We are sow - ing, ev-er sowing, Be the weath - er foul or fair;
3. We are sow - ing, ev-er sowing, In the home and on the street,

And the har - vest that shall follow, Shall a bane or blessing prove;
Heedless-ly how oft we scat-ter, Where there's need of great-est care;
Sow-ing good or sowing e - vil, For our-selves and all we meet;

Are we sow-ing thorns and thistles, That shall pierce the trav'ler's feet,
Now's the seed-time, full of promise, Full of pos - si-bil - i - ty;
Let us earn - est-ly en-deav-or Seeds of hap - - pi-ness to strew,

Or the seeds of love and mer-cy, That shall make ex-ist-ence sweet?
What the fruit - age we shall gather, Here and in...... e - ter - ni - ty?
That our fel - low-men may bless us, Whereso-ev - - er we may go.

CHORUS.

Sow-ing pain............. or sow-ing pleas - - ure,
Sow-ing pain or sow-ing pleasure, Sow-ing pain or sow-ing pleas-ure,

Sowing, Ever Sowing.

Sow-ing tares................ or gold-en wheat;
Sow-ing tares or gold-en wheat, yes, Sow-ing tares or gold-en wheat;

What, oh, what.......... .... shall be the har - - vest,
What, oh, what shall be the harvest, What, oh, what shall be the har-vest,

When our sow - - ing is com - plete?
When our sow-ing, when our sow-ing is com-plete, yes, is com-plete?

83 Nearer, Yet Nearer.

A. S. KIEFFER.

1. { Near-er, yet near-er, My God, to thee,
     Dear-er, yet dear-er, Thou art to me; } Still hop-ing, trust-ing,

2. { Pur-er, yet pur-er, I long to be,
     Near-er, yet near-er, My God, to thee; } Still hop-ing, pray-ing,

3. { High-er, yet high-er, Out of the night,
     Near-er, yet near-er, The throne of white, } Still ris-ing high-er,

Ev - er to be, Near - er, my Sav - ior, Near - er to thee.
Ev - er to be, Near - er, still near - er, My God to thee.
Near - er the light, Near - er, still near - er, The throne of white.

84 We Shall Stand Before the King.

E. O. E.

E. O. EXCELL.

1. We shall stand before the King, With the an-gels we shall sing, By and
2. Ring, ye bells of heaven, ring, We shall stand before the King, By and
3. Wake, my soul, thy tribute bring, Thou shalt stand before the King, By and

by, ... by and by; Walk the bright, the gold-en shore,
by, ... by and by; There our sor-rows will be o'er,
by, ... by and by; Lay thy tro-phies at his feet,

By and by, by and by,

Prais-ing him for ev-er-more, By and by, ... by and by.
There his name we will a-dore, By and by, ... by and by.
In his like-ness stand complete, By and by, ... by and by.

By and by, by and by

CHORUS.

We shall stand .... be-fore the King, ... With the

We shall stand be-fore the King,

angels we shall sing, Glory, glo-ry to our King, Halle-lu - - jah, hal-le-

Hal-le - lu-jah,

We shall Stand before the King.

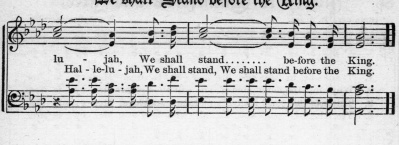

lu - jah, We shall stand........ be-fore the King.
Hal - le-lu - jah, We shall stand, We shall stand before the King.

85 Wonderful Love of Jesus.

E. D. Mund.

E. S. Lorenz.

1. In vain in high and ho - ly lays My soul her grateful voice would raise; For
2. A joy by day, a peace by night, In storms a calm, in darkness light, In
3. My hope for pardon when I call, My trust for lift - ing when I fall, In

who can sing the wor-thy praise Of the won-der-ful love of Je - sus?
pain a balm, in weakness might Is the won-der-ful love of Je - sus.
life, in death, my all in all, Is the won-der-ful love of Je - sus.

REFRAIN.

Won-der-ful love! won-der-ful love! Won-der-ful love of Je - sus!

Won-der-ful love! won-der-ful love! Won-der-ful love of Je - sus!

86. Mercy is Boundless and Free.

Henrietta E. Blair. Wm. J. Kirkpatrick.

1. Thanks be to Je-sus, his mer-cy is free, Mer-cy is free,
2. Why on the mountains of sin wilt thou roam? Mer-cy is free,
3. Think of his good-ness, his pa-tience and love; Mer-cy is free,
4. Yes, there is par-don for all who be-lieve; Mer-cy is free,

REFRAIN.—Je-sus the Sav-ior, is look-ing for thee, Look-ing for thee,

mer-cy is free: Sin-ner, that mer-cy is flow-ing for thee,
mer-cy is free: Gen-tly the Spir-it is call-ing, "Come home,"
mer-cy is free: Pleading thy cause with his Fa-ther a-bove,
mer-cy is free: Come, and this mo-ment a bless-ing re-ceive,

look-ing for thee; Lov-ing-ly, ten-der-ly call-ing for thee,

FINE.

Mer-cy is bound-less and free. If thou art will-ing on
Mer-cy is bound-less and free. Thou art in dark-ness, O,
Mer-cy is bound-less and free. Come and re-pent-ing, O,
Mer-cy is bound-less and free. Je-sus is wait-ing, O,

Call-ing and look-ing for thee.

him to be-lieve, Mer-cy is free, mer-cy is free;
come to the light, Mer-cy is free, mer-cy is free;
give him thy heart, Mer-cy is free, mer-cy is free;
hear him pro-claim Mer-cy is free, mer-cy is free;

Mercy Is Boundless.

D. C. REFRAIN.

Life ev-er-last-ing thy soul may re-ceive, Mercy is boundless and free.
Je-sus is waiting, he'll save you to-night, Mercy is boundless and free.
Grieve him no longer, but come as thou art, Mercy is boundless and free.
Cling to his mer-cy, believe on his name, Mercy is boundless and free.

87

Blessed be the Name.

CHARLES WESLEY.

R. E. HUDSON.

1. O for a thousand tongues to sing: Blessed be the name of the Lord!
2. Jesus, the name that charms our fears, Blessed be the name of the Lord!
3. He breaks the pow'r of cancelled sin, Blessed be the name of the Lord!

The glo - ries of my God and King, Blessed be the name of the Lord!
'Tis mu - sic in the sin - ner's ears, Blessed be the name of the Lord!
His blood can make the foul-est clean, Blessed be the name of the Lord!

CHORUS.

Blessed be the name, Blessed be the name, Blessed be the name of the Lord!

Blessed be the name, Blessed be the name, Blessed be the name of the Lord.

Look Away to the Cross.

J. E. RANKIN, D. D.   FRANK M. DAVIS.

1. Look a-way to the cross, leave thy burdens all there, All the sins that con-
2. Look a-way to the cross, leave thy burdens all there, In the course of the
3. Look a-way to the cross, leave thy burdens all there, At the cross where thy

demn, all the wrong, All thy bit - ter remorse, all thy grief and despair;
swift com-ing years, He will give needed grace, all thy troub-les will bear,
Sav - ior has died; All thy sins he will par-don, thy sorrow he'll share,

CHORUS.

Look a-way to the cross and be strong.
And like clouds he will scatter thy fears.   } Look a-way to the cross, it will
And for all of thy wants will provide.

ease thee of care, And the shad - ows will leave thy soul; Look a-

way to the cross, hum-bly kneeling in prayer, Only Christ can make thee whole.

89

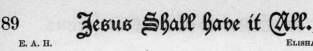

Jesus Shall have it All.

E. A. H.

ELISHA A. HOFFMAN.

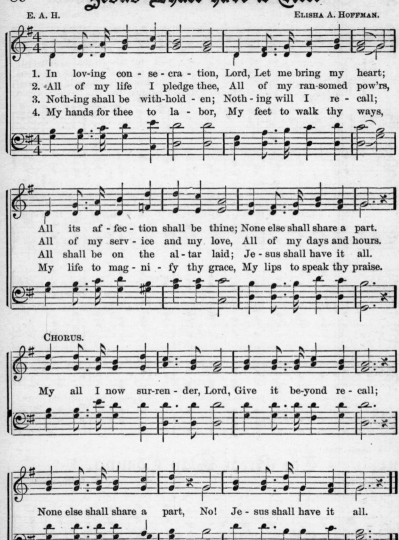

1. In lov-ing con - se - cra - tion, Lord, Let me bring my heart;
2. All of my life I pledge thee, All of my ran-somed pow'rs,
3. Noth-ing shall be with-hold - en; Noth - ing will I re - call;
4. My hands for thee to la - bor, My feet to walk thy ways,

All its af - fec - tion shall be thine; None else shall share a part.
All of my serv - ice and my love, All of my days and hours.
All shall be on the al - tar laid; Je - sus shall have it all.
My life to mag - ni - fy thy grace, My lips to speak thy praise.

CHORUS.

My all I now sur-ren - der, Lord, Give it be-yond re - call;

None else shall share a part, No! Je - sus shall have it all.

5 I should have served thee better,
I should have loved thee more;
Now I will live for thee alone,
Henceforth and evermore.

6 Here, at this holy altar,
Now, while in tears I bow,
Seal thou the covenant I make,
Hear and accept my vow.

90 'Tis so Sweet to Trust in Jesus.

Mrs. Louisa M. R. Stead.   Wm. J. Kirkpatrick.

1. 'Tis so sweet to trust in Je-sus, Just to take him at his word;
2. O how sweet to trust in Je-sus, Just to trust his cleansing blood;
3. Yes, 'tis sweet to trust in Je-sus, Just from sin and self to cease;
4. I'm so glad I learn'd to trust thee, Precious Je-sus, Savior, Friend;

Just to rest up-on his promise; Just to know, "Thus saith the Lord,"
Just in sim-ple faith to plunge me 'Neath the healing, cleansing flood.
Just from Je-sus simp-ly tak-ing Life and rest, and joy and peace.
And I know that thou art with me, Wilt be with me to the end.

Refrain.

Je-sus, Je-sus, how I trust him! How I've proved him o'er and o'er!

Je-sus, Je-sus, pre-cious Je-sus! O for grace to trust him more.

From "Songs of Triumph," by per.

91 The Great Day Coming.

W. L. T.   W. L. Thompson.

1. There's a great day com-ing, A great day com-ing, There's a
2. There's a bright day com-ing, A bright day com-ing, There's a
3. There's a sad day com-ing, A sad day com-ing, There's a

great day coming by and by, When the saints and the sin-ners shall be
bright day coming by and by, But the brightness shall on-ly come to
sad day coming by and by, When the sin-ner shall hear his doom, "de-

By per. W. L. Thompson & Co., East Liverpool, Ohio.   86

The Great Day Coming.

part - ed right and left; Are you read - y for that day to come?
those who love the Lord; Are you read - y for that day to come?
part, I know ye not; "Are you read - y for that day to come?"

m Chorus. *pp*   *m*

Are you read - y? Are you read - y? Are you read - y for the

m   *pp*   *m*

judgment day? Are you ready? Are you ready For the judgment day?

92 We Are Passing Away.

J. HART. *(Common Meter.)* Arr. by W. J. K.

1. { Vain man, thy fond pursuits for-bear; Re-pent, thine end is nigh;
   Death, at the far-thest, can't be far: O think be - fore thou die. }

REFRAIN

We are passing away, We are passing away, We are passing away To the great judgment day.

2 Reflect, thou hast a soul to save;
  Thy sins, how high they mount!
  What are thy hopes beyond the grave?
  How stands that dark account?

3 Death enters, and there's no defence;
  His time there's none can tell;

He'll in a moment call thee hence,
To heaven, or down to hell.

4 Thy flesh (perhaps thy greatest care)
  Shall into dust consume;
  But, ah! destruction ends not there;
  Sin kills beyond the tomb.

93 Scattering Precious Seed.

W. A. OGDEN.　　　　　　　　　　　　　　　　　GEO. C. HUGG.

1. Scat-ter-ing precious seed by the way-side,　Scatter-ing precious seed
2. Scat-ter-ing precious seed for the grow-ing,　Scatter-ing precious seed,
3. Scat-ter-ing precious seed, doubting nev-er,　Scatter-ing precious seed,

by the hill-side;　Scat-ter-ing pre-cious seed o'er the field, wide,
free-ly sow-ing;　Scat-ter-ing pre-cious seed, trusting, knowing,
trusting ev-er;　Sow-ing the word with pray'r and endeav-or,

CHORUS.

Scat-ter-ing precious seed by the way.　Sow - - ing in the
Sure-ly the Lord will send it the rain.　Sow - - ing in the
Trusting the Lord for growth and for yield.　Sowing the precious seed,

morn - - - ing,　Sow - - - ing at the
ev - - - 'ning,
Sow-ing the pre-cious seed,　Sow-ing the seed　at noon-tide,

noon - - tide;　Sowing the precious seed by the way.......
Sowing the precious seed;　　　　　　　　　　　by the way.

The Sheltering Rock.

W. E. P.

W. E. PENN.

Slow. May be sung with good effect as a Solo.

1. There is a Rock in a wea-ry land, Its shad-ow falls on the
2. There is a Well in a des-ert plain, Its wa-ters call with en-
3. A great fold stands with its por-tals wide, The sheep a-stray on the
4. There is a cross where the Sav-ior died, His blood flow'd out in a

burn-ing sand, In-vit-ing pilgrims as they pass To seek a shade in the
treating strain, "Ho, ev'ry thirsting sin-sick soul, Come freely drink, and thou
mountain side, The Shepherd climbs o'er mountains steep, He's searching now for his
crim-son tide, A sac-ri-fice for sins of men, And free to all who will

REFRAIN.

wil - der-ness.
shalt be whole."
wand'ring sheep.
en - ter in.

} Then why will ye die? Oh! why will ye die?

Slower.

When the shelt'ring Rock is so near by? Oh! why will ye die?
When the liv-ing Well is so near by? Oh! why will ye die?
When the Shepherd's fold is so near by? Oh! why will ye die?
When the crim-son cross is so near by? Oh! why will ye die?

What A Savior!

F. M. D.

FRANK. M. DAVIS.

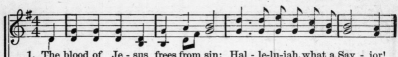

1. The blood of Je - sus frees from sin; Hal - le-lu-jah, what a Sav - ior!
2. Sal - va - tion, oh, that joy - ful sound! Hal - le-lu-jah, what a Sav - ior!
3. A - rise! a - rise! thy light is come! Hal - le-lu-jah, what a Sav - ior!

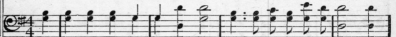

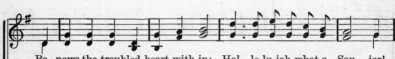

Re - news the troubled heart with-in; Hal - le-lu-jah, what a Sav - ior!
It reach-es earth's re - mot-est bound; Hal - le-lu-jah, what a Sav - ior!
Why sit ye long - er i - dle, dumb? Hal - le-lu-jah, what a Sav - ior!

His life he gave up - on a tree, That sin - ful man redeemed might be,
Triumphant raise the joy-ful strain, A Sav - ior dies but lives a - gain,
Proclaim a-broad his matchless name, Whose pow'r the vilest can re - claim,

And live thro' all e - ter - ni - ty, Hal - le-lu-jah, what a Sav - ior!
E - ter - nal in the heav'ns to reign, Hal - le-lu-jah, what a Sav - ior!
Thro'out e - ter - ni - ty the same, Hal - le-lu-jah, what a Sav - ior!

The Beautiful Light.

R. Kelso Carter.

Jno. R. Sweney.

1. Je - sus is the light, the way, We are walking in the light, We are
2. We who know our sins for-given, We are walking in the light, We are
3. As we jour - ney here be - low, We are walking in the light, We are
4. We will sing his power to save, We are walking in the light, We are

walking in the light; Shining brighter day by day, We are walking in the
walking in the light; Find on earth the joy of heav'n, We are walking in the
walking in the light; Oh, what joy and peace we know, We are walking in the
walking in the light; We will triumph o'er the grave, We are walking in the

Refrain.

beautiful light of God. We are walk - ing in the light, We are
Walking in the light, beautiful light of God,

walk - ing in the light, We are walk - ing in the
Walking in the light, beautiful light of God, Walking in the light,

light,............ We are walking in the beautiful light of God.
Walking in the light,

97 Walking and Talking With Jesus.

Eben E. Rexford.

W. E. Penn.

1. When I read the dear old sto - ry of the Cross and Cal - va - ry,
2. Oh, to walk and talk with Je - sus, what a rap - ture in the tho't!
3. I can walk and talk with Je - sus, tho' I can not see his face;

With what joy my heart runs o - ver, as I think he died for me;
Oh, to be like his dis - ci - ples, by the world's great teacher taught!
I can feel the Lord who loves me near in ev - 'ry time and place;

And my soul is filled with long-ing, as I read that long a - go,
And my heart o'er-flows with gladness, as the sto - ry I re - peat;
I can feel his smile up - on me, "Fol-low me," I hear him say;

Persons walked and talked with Je-sus as he journeyed to and fro.
Let me walk and talk with Je - sus, let me learn at Je - sus' feet.
Soul, be glad—with those who love him, Je - sus walks and talks to - day.

CHORUS.

Oh, to walk and talk with Je - sus, 'Tis a bless-ed tho't to me.

Walking With Jesus.

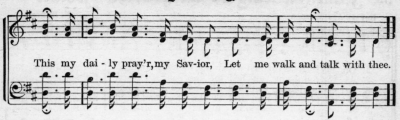

This my dai-ly pray'r, my Sav-ior, Let me walk and talk with thee.

98 Where Will You Spend Eternity?

Rev. E. A. HOFFMAN.   J. H. TENNEY.

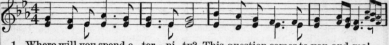

1. Where will you spend e - ter - ni - ty? This question comes to you and me!
2. Ma - ny are choosing Christ to-day, Turning from all their sins a-way;
3. Leav-ing the strait and narrow way, Go - ing the downward road to-day,
4. Re - pent, believe, this ver - y hour, Trust in the Savior's grace and pow'r,

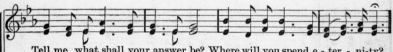

Tell me, what shall your answer be? Where will you spend e - ter - ni-ty?
Heav'n shall their hap-py por - tion be, Where will you spend e - ter - ni-ty?
Sad will their fi - nal end - ing be,—Lost thro' a long e - ter - ni-ty?
Then will your joyous an-swer be, Saved thro' a long e - ter - ni-ty!

REFRAIN.

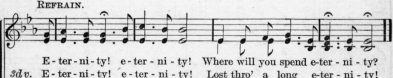

E - ter - ni - ty! e - ter - ni - ty! Where will you spend e-ter - ni - ty?
3d v. E - ter - ni - ty! e - ter - ni - ty! Lost thro' a long e-ter - ni - ty!
4th v. E - ter - ni - ty! e - ter - ni - ty! Saved thro' a long e-ter - ni - ty!

99 I am Resting in the Savior's Love.

Rev. E. A. HOFFMAN.   D. E. DORTCH.

1. Oh, my heart is thrilled with wondrous joy to-day, I am resting in the
2. At the fount-ain o-pened for the soul un-clean, I am resting in the
3. All my doubts are vanished, all my fears are gone, I am resting in the
4. O the peace and rapt-ure! O the wondrous bliss! I am resting in the
5. So I live re-joic-ing in his love each day, I am resting in the

Sav-ior's love; Christ, the Lord, has tak-en all my sins a-way, I am
Sav-ior's love; Trust-ing in his grace I ventured free-ly in, I am
Sav-ior's love; When I trust-ed Je-sus, lo, the work was done! I am
Sav-ior's love; I have nev-er known so pure a joy as this; I am
Sav-ior's love; I am walking with him in the nar-row way, I am

REFRAIN.

rest-ing in the Savior's love.   I am resting, sweet - ly resting,
                                  I am resting, resting, sweetly resting,

I am rest-ing in the Sav-ior's love;   I am rest-ing,

sweet - ly resting,   I am resting in the Sav-ior's love.
resting, sweet-ly resting,

94

Power to Save.

W. A. O.

W. A. OGDEN.

1. There's a song my heart is sing-ing, In my soul its tones are ring-ing,
2. Oh, that song my soul is thrilling, Je-sus saves the soul that's willing!
3. Sin-ner, come, if thou'lt receive him, Look to Je-sus and be-lieve him,

Peace and rest and joy 'tis bring-ing, Je-sus Christ has power to save!
Pre-cious truth! my heart 'tis fill-ing, Je-sus Christ has power to save!
All your life and serv-ice give him, Je-sus Christ has power to save!

CHORUS. (SOLO, BASS OBLIGATO.)

Sing it o-ver and o-ver a-gain to me.

Sing it o'er..... a-gain to me..... In its

Cres.

In its won-der-ful sweet sim-plic-i-ty; Tell it

sweet..... sim-plic-i-ty;.......

o'er.... the o-cean wave, Je-sus Christ.. has power to save.
Tell it o'er the o-cean wave, Je-sus Christ has power to save.

When we Reach our Home.

E. A. H.

Rev. Elisha A. Hoffman.

1. What a scene of wondrous glo - ry, When we reach our home, Chanting
2. We shall know no more of tri - al, When we reach our home, Nor of
3. We will meet our pre-cious Sav - ior When we reach our home, Live for-

there redemption's sto-ry, 'Neath its gold-en dome! With myr-iads round the throne,
toil and self - de - ni - al, 'Neath its gold-en dome; In robes of pu - ri-ty,
ev - er in his fa - vor 'Neath the gold-en dome; Changed to his likeness, we

His a-noint - ed and his own, We will make his prais - es known,
From all sin and sor - row free, Safe with Je - sus we will be
Shall his glo-rious per - son see, And a - dore him cease-less - ly

CHORUS.

When we reach our home.
In our heav'n-ly home. } When we reach our home o-ver there, o-ver there,
In our heav'n-ly home.

All the wondrous glo - ry to share, What a meet-ing that will be
o - ver there,

When We Reach Our Home.

Christ and his redeemed to see, When we reach our home over there, o-ver there!

102 We'll Never Say Good-By.

Mrs. E. W. CHAPMAN.

J. H. TENNEY.

1. With friends on earth we meet in gladness, While swift the moments fly,
2. How joy-ful is the hope that lin-gers, When loved ones cross death's sea,
3. No part-ing words shall e'er be spok-en In yon-der home so fair,

Yet ev-er comes the tho't of sad-ness, That we must say, "Good-by."
That we, when all earth's toils are end-ed, With thee shall ev-er be.
But songs of joy, and peace, and gladness, We'll sing for-ev-er there.

CHORUS.

We'll never say good-by in heav'n, We'll nev-er say good-by, (good-by,)

Repeat Chorus pp.

For in that land of joy and song We'll nev-er say good-by.

They Crucified Him.

J. M. W.

J. M. WHYTE. Arr.

1. Come, sin-ner, be-hold what Je-sus hath done,
2. From heav-en he came, he loved you— he died:
3. No pit-y-ing eye, a sav-ing arm, none,
4. They cru-ci-fied him, and yet he for-gave,
5. So what will you do with Je-sus your King?

Be-hold how he suf-fered for thee: They cru-ci-fied him,
Such love as his nev-er was known; Be-hold on the cross
He saw us and pit-ied us then; A-lone in the fight,
"My Fa-ther, for-give them," he cried; What must he have borne,
Say, how will you meet him at last? What plea in the day

God's in-no-cent Son, For-sak-en, he died on the tree!
your King cru-ci-fied, To make you an heir to his throne!
the vic-t'ry he won; O praise him, ye chil-dren of men.
the sin-ner to save, When un-der the bur-den he died!
of wrath will you bring, When of-fers of mer-cy are past?

CHORUS.

They cru-ci-fied him, they crucified him, They nailed him to the tree,

And there he died, A King cru-ci-fied To save a poor sinner like me, like me.

104 Beneath Thy Shadow Hiding.

J. E. RANKIN, D. D.   J. H. TENNEY.

1. Be-neath thy shadow hid-ing, I sing my pil-grim song; Brief here is
2. I'm naught, dear Lord, without thee, But feeble, falt'ring clay; Throw thy strong
3. Thou hast my ransom paid me, The wine-press for me trod, In faith's fair

my a-bid-ing, My stay can-not be long; Thus far thy hand hath
arms a-bout me, And cheer me on my way. What-ev-er lot be-
robe ar-rayed me, Now bring me home to God. While thou art there pre-

brought me, And I am far-ing on To where thy word has taught me, My
tide me, This thing I sure-ly know: Sal-vation's stream beside me Shall
par-ing For my poor soul a place, Thus heav'nward am I far-ing, To

CHORUS.

Lord, him-self, is gone. }
still un-fail-ing flow.   } Beneath thy shadow hid-ing, I sing my
see thee face to face.   }

pil-grim song, My all to thee con-fid-ing, To whom I all be-long.

Lo! A Mighty Army.

Rev. H. G. Jackson.　　　　　　　　　　　　Arr. by Chas. H. Gabriel.

1. Lo! a might-y ar-my now as-sem-bling, Rally-ing to the
2. Marshalled league of ea-ger, youthful sol-diers, Girt with truth they
3. Fierce and long may be the dire-ful con-flict With the host of

cross, a might-y band, Bold to strive against the pow'rs of e-vil,
bear the Spir-it's sword, Shield of faith and hel-met of sal-va-tion,
un-be-lief and sin; Fal-ter not, but swift go forth to bat-tle,

CHORUS.

Sworn to do or die at God's command. For-ward, ye sol-diers of Je-sus,
Read-y, waiting for the Captain's word.
Truth and right with God the fight will win. Forward, forward, march, ye soldiers,

With his banner o'er you, Charge the foe be-fore you; Val-iant-ly
For-ward, for-ward, march, ye sol-diers, Forward, march, ye

fol-low your captain, Till the fight with sin is o'er; For-ward, ye
sol-diers, for-ward, Forward, forward,

Lo! A Mighty Army.

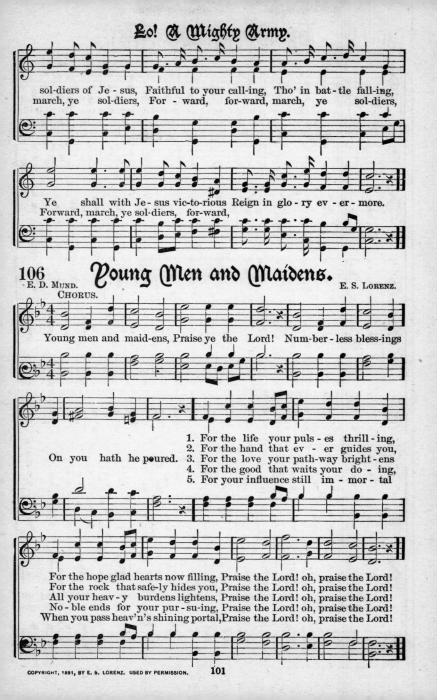

sol-diers of Je - sus, Faithful to your call-ing, Tho' in bat - tle fall-ing,
march, ye sol-diers, For - ward, for-ward, march, ye sol-diers,

Ye shall with Je - sus vic-to-rious Reign in glo - ry ev - er - more.
Forward, march, ye sol-diers, for-ward,

106 Young Men and Maidens.

E. D. MUND.   E. S. LORENZ.

CHORUS.

Young men and maid-ens, Praise ye the Lord! Num-ber-less bless-ings

On you hath he poured.

1. For the life your puls - es thrill - ing,
2. For the hand that ev - er guides you,
3. For the love your path-way bright - ens,
4. For the good that waits your do - ing,
5. For your influence still im - mor - tal

For the hope glad hearts now filling, Praise the Lord! oh, praise the Lord!
For the rock that safe-ly hides you, Praise the Lord! oh, praise the Lord!
All your heav - y burdens lightens, Praise the Lord! oh, praise the Lord!
No - ble ends for your pur - su - ing, Praise the Lord! oh, praise the Lord!
When you pass heav'n's shining portal, Praise the Lord! oh, praise the Lord!

He Blessed Me There.

Lanta Wilson Smith. Effective as a Solo. J. H. Tenney.

1. When deep in sin and fol - ly My feet had gone a-stray, A voice of
2. I sought my mother's Bi - ble, And searched its pages o'er, To find the
3. My soul knows well it's Bethel Where God spoke peace to me; The ver - y
4. Oh, all a-long my pathway What al - tars I may rear, With this in-

warn-ing led me To seek the bet-ter way; The bur-den of my
shin-ing path-way That saints have trod be-fore; I found a-bun-dant
gate of heav-en It ev - er-more must be; I've wrestled thro' the
scrip-tion on - ly: "Christ came and blessed me there!" And when mid heaven's

sor-row Was more than I could bear, I sought the shrine of mer-cy, He
rich-es Of grace that all may share, And while I read those pages, Christ
midnight Of doubt, and pain, and care, But always ere the dawning Christ
glo-ries A crown of life I wear, I'll tell how thro' earth's conflicts Christ

Chorus.

came and blessed me there. Oh, praise His name forev-er! The Savior blessed me
He

there! In life and death I'll praise Him, Because He blessed me there!
blessed me there!

Workers for the Master.

W. A. O.

W. A. OGDEN.

1. Earn-est work-ers for the Mas-ter, Send the word a-long the line:
2. Earn-est work-ers grace he giv-eth, Grace for ev-'ry time of need;
3. Earn-est work-ers, up in heav-en There a-waits for you a crown,
4. Earn-est work-ers, true and loy-al To the Lord, oh, let us be!

We shall nev-er know dis-as-ter, Trust-ing in the pow'r di-vine.
While the God of glo-ry liv-eth, They shall on his man-na feed.
Which the Lord him-self will give you When you lay your ar-mor down.
As we go in ser-vice roy-al, Let us shout the Ju-bi-lee.

CHORUS.

Hal-le-lu-jah! hal-le-lu-jah! Prais-es sing to God on high!

And to Je-sus who hath bought us, Let the glo-rious an-them fly.

109 Quit You Like Men.

E. A. H.

Rev. Elisha A. Hoffman.

1. Be strong to toil in the vineyard wide, And in the serv-ice of
2. Be strong to take up your dai - ly cross, And bear for Christ a - ny
3. Be strong to bat - tle a-gainst all sin, The foes with-out and the
4. Be brave and faithful, and cour-age take; Nev - er, no, nev - er your

Christ a - bide; A rich re-ward you at last shall win,
pain or loss, Un - til, the bur - dens of life laid down,
foes with - in; Con - quer by faith in the cleans-ing blood,
Lord for - sake; Fight till the con - flict on earth is done;

CHORUS.

When all the sheaves shall be gath-ered in.
Je - sus shall give you a fade - less crown.
Con - quer the world by the help of God.
Fight till the vic - t'ry thro' Christ is won.

Quit you like men, be

strong! The fight may be fierce and long, But in God's
Be strong! ver - y long,

strength we shall win at length; Then quit you like men, be strong!
be strong!

110 Trust and Obey.

Rev. J. H. SAMMIS.   D. B. TOWNER.

1. When we walk with the Lord In the light of his Word, What a glo-ry he
2. Not a sha-dow can rise, Not a cloud in the skies, But his smile quickly
3. Not a bur-den we bear, Not a sor-row we share, But our toil he doth

sheds on our way! While we do his good will, He a-bides with us
drives it a-way; Not a doubt nor a fear, Not a sigh nor a
rich-ly re-pay; Not a grief nor a loss, Not a frown nor a

CHORUS.

still, And with all who will trust and o-bey. Trust and o-bey, For there's
tear Can abide while we trust and o-bey.
cross, But is blest if we trust and o-bey.

no oth-er way To be hap-py in Je-sus But to trust and o-bey.

4 But we never can prove
    The delights of his love
Until all on the altar we lay,
    For the favor he shows,
    And the joy he bestows,
Are for all who will trust and obey.

5 Then in fellowship sweet
    We will sit at his feet,
Or we'll walk by his side in the way;
    What he says we will do,
    Where he sends we will go,
Never fear, only trust and obey.

111 Idle Stand Not all the Day.

J. E. Rankin, D. D.

W. A. Ogden.

1. There's a place where we may la - bor, One and all (One and all);
2. "In the mar - ket i - dly stand-ing, Are there more (Are there more)"
3. And the Mas - ter still is wait - ing, Call - ing still (Calling still):

To the har - vest fields that rip - en, Hear the call (Hear the call);
Calls the Mas - ter of the har - vest, O'er and o'er (O'er and o'er);
"Go ye all in - to my vine-yard, With a will (With a will);

I - dle stand not all the day, Stow the Mas-ter's grain a - way;
Calls the Mas - ter, far and near: "I - dle stand no long - er here,
Be it ear - ly, be it late, I - dle there no long - er wait,

It is read - y for the gar - ner, Why de - lay (Why de-lay)?
I will give you righteous wa - ges, Nev - er fear (Nev-er fear)."
What is right I sure will give you, Great and small (Great and small)."

CHORUS.

Why de - lay? Haste a - way, Soon will come settling day; While the

106

Idle Stand Not all the Day.

golden harvests wait Ripe to fall (Ripe to fall); Stand not at the market gate, Hear, oh, hear the Master's call: "Work you my desire, I'll give, will give you hire (give you hire)."

112

Enough for Me.

E. A. H.

ELISHA A. HOFFMAN.

1. O love surpassing knowledge! O grace so full and free! I know that Jesus saves me, And

FINE. REFRAIN

D. S.

that's enough for me! And that's enough for me! And that's enough for me! I

2 O wonderful salvation!
  From sin he makes me free!
I have the sweet assurance,
  And that's enough for me!

3 O blood of Christ so precious,
  Poured out on Calvary'
I feel its cleansing power,
  And that's enough for me!

113 Sweet Peace, the Gift of God's Love.

P. P. BILHORN.

PETER BILHORN.

1. There comes to my heart one sweet strain (sweet strain), A
2. By Christ on the cross peace was made (was made), My
3. When Je-sus as Lord I had crowned (had crowned), My
4. In Je-sus for peace I a-bide (a-bide), And

glad and a joy-ous re-frain (re-frain), I sing it a-
debt by his death was all paid (all paid), No oth-er foun-
heart with this peace did a-bound (a-bound), In him the rich
as I keep close to his side (his side), There's noth-ing but

gain and a-gain, Sweet peace, the gift of God's love.
da-tion is laid For peace, the gift of God's love.
bless-ing I found, Sweet peace, the gift of God's love.
peace doth be-tide, Sweet peace, the gift of God's love.

CHORUS.

Peace, peace, sweet peace! Won-der-ful gift from a-bove (a-bove)! Oh,

won-der-ful, won-der-ful peace! Sweet peace, the gift of God's love!

114 My Rock and Shield.

JESSE L. SPORE.

W. A. OGDEN.

1. I know not why God's love and mighty pow'r To me he hath re - vealed;
2. His mercy smoothes my rough and ston-y way O'er life's dark pathway dim;
3. And when affliction's rod and heavy hand Is laid up-on me sore,

But this I know, in ev'ry try - ing hour He is my rock and shield.
He is my rock and sure defense each day, My trust is all in him.
I put my faith and trust in him, for he Is life for - ev - er - more.

CHORUS.

He is my rock............ and sure de - fense;..... ......
He is my rock   and sure de-fense;

My all to him....... I yield, For this I know, in
To Him I yield,

ev - 'ry try - ing hour, He is my rock and shield.

115 Linger No Longer.

E. A. H.

Rev. Elisha A. Hoffman.

1. Lin-ger no long-er, Je-sus is wait-ing, Wait-ing to cleanse your soul;
2. Lin-ger no long-er, an-gels are wait-ing, Wait-ing to see you come;
3. Lin-ger no long-er, lov'd ones are wait-ing, Wait-ing the while they pray;
4. Lin-ger no long-er, mer-cy is flow-ing, Flow-ing so rich and free;
5. Lin-ger no long-er, this is the mo-ment Of God's re-demp-tive pow'r;

Lin-ger no long-er, Je-sus is wait-ing, Wait-ing to make you whole.
Lin-ger no long-er, an-gels are wait-ing To bear the ti-dings home.
Lin-ger no long-er, lov'd ones are wait-ing For your re-turn to-day.
Lin-ger no long-er, mer-cy is flow-ing, And you may pardoned be.
Lin-ger no long-er, lin-ger no long-er, This is sal-va-tion's hour.

CHORUS.

Lin-ger no long-er, come, come to Je-sus, O-pen is mer-cy's gate;

Lin-ger no long-er, come, come to Je-sus Ere it may be too late.

116 I've been Washed in the Blood.

W. T. Dale.　　　　　　　　　　　　　　　　　　D. E. Dortch.

1. I have been to Je-sus, he has cleansed my soul, I've been washed in the
2. I am dai-ly trust-ing Je-sus at my side, I've been washed in the
3. I am working in the vineyard of the Lord, I've been washed in the
4. I am list'ning now to hear the Bridegroom's voice, I've been washed in the

blood of the Lamb; By the precious fountain I have been made whole,
blood of the Lamb; I am sweet-ly rest-ing in the Cru-ci-fied,
blood of the Lamb; I am trust-ing in the prom-ise of his word,
blood of the Lamb; How his com-ing will each faith-ful heart re-joice!

CHORUS.

I've been washed in the blood of the Lamb. I've been washed, I've been
　　　　　　　　　　　　　　　　　　　　　　　　in the blood,

washed, I've been washed in the blood of the Lamb; And my robe is
in the blood,　　　　　　　　　　　　　　　　of the Lamb;

spotless, it is white as snow, I've been washed in the blood of the Lamb.

117 Sing of the Mighty One.

F. R. HAVERGAL.   W. A. OGDEN.

1. When light di-vine had touched the hills, By slumb'ring Gal-i-lee,
2. And when they brought the suff'ring ones, The low-ly and the dear,
3. He heard the prayer and gave the will And strength to touch the hem,
4. Oh, ten-der One, oh, might-y One, Who nev-er sent a-way

The gold-en wave then roll'd a-far To-wards the west-ern sea,
And laid them at the Heal-er's feet, From far a-way and near,
And gave the faith, and vir-tue flowed From Him and heal-èd them,
The sin-ner, or the suf-fer-er, Thou art the same to-day,

And when the men had knowledge of The Ho-ly One of God,
They bent be-fore the wondrous One, And earn-est-ly be-sought,
For ev-'ry one whose feeblest touch Thus met the Sav-ior's pow'r,
The same in love, the same in pow'r, And thou art wait-ing still

They journeyed forth thro' all the land, And spread his fame a-broad.
That they might on-ly touch the hem A-round his garment wrought.
Rose up in per-fect health and strength In that ac-cept-ed hour.
To heal the mul-ti-tude that come, Yea, who-so-ev-er will.

CHORUS. Spirited.

O sing of the lov-ing One! O sing of the heal-ing One!

Sing of the Mighty One.

O sing of the might-y One, He's just the same to-day!

118

Grace is Free.

J. S. N.

J. S. NORRIS.

SOLO.   CHORUS.

1. The voice of Christ to thee is cry-ing "Grace is free! Grace is free!
   O come to me, ye sad and dy-ing, Grace is free! Grace is free!"
2. Our Fa-ther now to thee is call-ing "Grace is free! Grace is free!"
   O hear his ac-cents gen-tly fall-ing, Grace is free! Grace is free!
3. Our loved in glo-ry now are sing-ing "Grace is free! Grace is free!"
   And heaven's bells with joy are ring-ing "Grace is free! Grace is free!"

DUET.

O glo-ry in the sa-cred cross, And count all oth-er things but loss,
He knows thy grief, he hears thy moan, He'll welcome thee, no longer roam,
The Spirit pleads with thee to-day, O come to Christ without de-lay,

CHORUS.

The best be-side is naught but dross, Grace is free! Grace is free!
The feast is spread for thee at home, Grace is free! Grace is free!
He is the truth, the life, the way! Grace is free! Grace is free!

119 I'll Lend a Hand.

Lanta Wilson Smith.
March Movement.

J. H. Tenney.

1. I've heard the call ring-ing far and wide: "Who'll come and work for the
2. I'll lend a hand in the church of God, Some work is wait-ing for
3. O let us work while the days go by, Striv-ing to light-en the

Lord to-day? Who'll feed the hun-gry and clothe the poor? Who'll
me to do; Read-y for serv-ice or sac-ri-fice, I'll
world's dispair, Win-ning the hearts that are filled with sin, Leav-

CHORUS.

find the lost that are gone a-stray?"
join the ranks of the faith-ful few. } I'll lend a hand in the
ing the joy of sal-va-tion there!

work of the Lord; I've heard the call, and read-y I stand; Glad-

ly to seek and to res-cue the lost, I'll lend a hand, lend a hand.

My Sins Are Taken Away.

HORATIUS BONAR, D. D.

J. H. TENNEY.

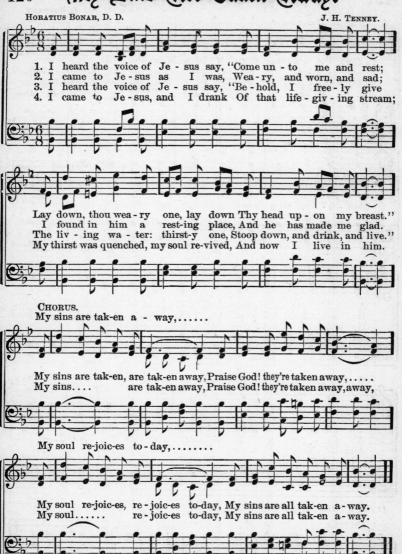

1. I heard the voice of Je-sus say, "Come un-to me and rest;
2. I came to Je-sus as I was, Wea-ry, and worn, and sad;
3. I heard the voice of Je-sus say, "Be-hold, I free-ly give
4. I came to Je-sus, and I drank Of that life-giv-ing stream;

Lay down, thou wea-ry one, lay down Thy head up-on my breast."
I found in him a rest-ing place, And he has made me glad.
The liv-ing wa-ter: thirst-y one, Stoop down, and drink, and live."
My thirst was quenched, my soul re-vived, And now I live in him.

CHORUS.

My sins are tak-en a-way,......

My sins are tak-en, are tak-en away, Praise God! they're taken away,.....
My sins.... are tak-en away, Praise God! they're taken away, away,

My soul re-joic-es to-day,........

My soul re-joic-es, re-joic-es to-day, My sins are all tak-en a-way.
My soul...... re-joic-es to-day, My sins are all tak-en a-way.

5 I heard the voice of Jesus say,
  "I am this dark world's light;
Look unto me, thy morn shall rise
And all thy day be bright."

6 I looked to Jesus, and I found
  In him my Star, my Sun;
And in that light of life I'll walk
Till all my journey's done.

121. Oh, the Glad, Good News!

E. A. H.

Rev. Elisha A. Hoffman.

1. Hear the mes-sage from a-bove, Won-der-ful the news!
2. Je-sus took the sin-ner's place, Oh, the pre-cious news!
3. Have you heard of Je-sus' power, Oh, the gra-cious news!

God be-stows on us his love, Won-der-ful the news!
Of-fers now to all his grace, Oh, the pre-cious news!
Man-i-fest each pass-ing hour? Oh, the gra-cious news!

All earth's weary ones are blest Who have Je-sus Christ confessed;
He a-toned on Cal-va-ry, From my sins to ran-som me,
He has come to my poor soul, My af-fec-tions to con-trol,

FINE.

Je-sus gives them peace and rest, Won-der-ful the news!
To for-ev-er set me free; Oh, the pre-cious news!
And his blood has made me whole; Oh, the gra-cious news!

D.S. On the tree Christ died for me, Oh, the glad, good news!

CHORUS.

D. S. al FINE.

Oh, the bless-ed mes-sage! Oh, the gra-cious news!

A Mighty Fortress.

MARTIN LUTHER. Tr. by F. H. HEDGE.   MARTIN LUTHER.

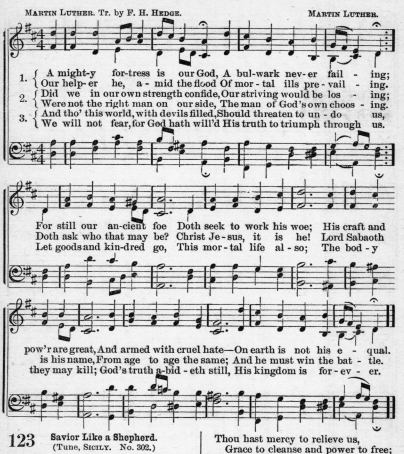

1. A might-y for-tress is our God, A bul-wark nev-er fail - ing;
   Our help-er he, a - mid the flood Of mor - tal ills pre - vail - ing.
2. Did we in our own strength confide, Our striving would be los - ing;
   Were not the right man on our side, The man of God's own choos - ing.
3. And tho' this world, with devils filled, Should threaten to un - do us,
   We will not fear, for God hath will'd His truth to triumph through us.

For still our an-cient foe Doth seek to work his woe; His craft and
Doth ask who that may be? Christ Je-sus, it is he! Lord Sabaoth
Let goods and kin-dred go, This mor - tal life al - so; The bod - y

pow'r are great, And armed with cruel hate—On earth is not his e - qual.
is his name, From age to age the same; And he must win the bat - tle.
they may kill; God's truth a-bid - eth still, His kingdom is for - ev - er.

123 **Savior Like a Shepherd.**
(Tune, SICILY. No. 302.)

1 Savior, like a shepherd lead us,
   Much we need thy tend'rest care,
In thy pleasant pastures feed us,
   For our use thy folds prepare;
‖: Blessed Jesus, blessed Jesus,
Thou hast bought us; thine we are. :‖

2 We are thine, do thou befriend us,
   Be the Guardian of our way;
Keep thy flock, from sin defend us,
   Seek us when we go astray;
‖: Blessed Jesus, blessed Jesus,
   Hear, oh, hear us, when we pray. :‖

3 Thou hast promised to receive us,
   Poor and sinful though we be;

Thou hast mercy to relieve us,
   Grace to cleanse and power to free;
‖: Blessed Jesus, blessed Jesus,
We will early turn to thee. :‖

DOROTHY A. THRUPP.

124 **To Thee be Praise.**
(Tune, WEBB. No. 264.)

To thee be praise forever,
   Thou glorious King of Kings!
Thy wondrous love and favor
   Each ransomed spirit sings:
We'll celebrate thy glory,
   With all thy saints above,
And shout the joyful story
   Of thy redeeming love.

THOMAS HAWEIS.

125 Resting Safe with Jesus.

VICTORIA E. KEITH.   W. A. OGDEN.

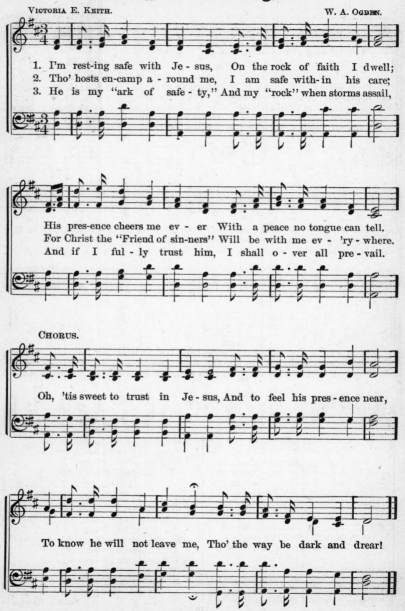

1. I'm rest-ing safe with Je - sus,   On the rock of faith I dwell;
2. Tho' hosts en-camp a - round me,   I am safe with-in his care;
3. He is my "ark of safe - ty," And my "rock" when storms assail,

His pres-ence cheers me ev - er   With a peace no tongue can tell.
For Christ the "Friend of sin-ners" Will be with me ev - 'ry - where.
And if I ful - ly trust him, I shall o - ver all pre - vail.

CHORUS.

Oh, 'tis sweet to trust in Je - sus, And to feel his pres - ence near,

To know he will not leave me, Tho' the way be dark and drear!

126 Lead Me, Savior.

F. M. D.

FRANK M. DAVIS.

With expression.

1. Sav-ior, lead me, lest I stray, Gen-tly lead me all the
2. Thou the refuge of my soul When life's storm-y bil-lows
3. Sav-ior, lead me, then at last, When the storm of life is

1. Sav-ior, lead me, lest I stray, Gen-tly

way; I am safe when by thy side,
roll, I am safe when thou art nigh,
past, To the land of end-less day,

lead me all the way; I am safe when by thy side,

CHORUS.

I would in thy love a-bide.
All my hopes on thee re-ly.
Where all tears are wiped a-way. Lead me, lead me,

I would in thy love a-bide.

Sav-ior, lead me, lest I stray; .... Gen-tly down the stream of
lest I stray;

Rit. e dim.

time, (stream of time,) Lead me, Sav-ior, all the way, (all the way.)

127 Hear the Bugle Calling.

Mrs. E. Whitaker John.

D. C. John.

1. Hear the bu - gle call - ing, Come with-out de - lay; Arm you, Christian
2. Christ, the conquering He-ro, Wa - ges war with sin, And He needs brave
3. Sa - tan's host now trembling, Can-not long - er stand; Tho' the con-flict

sol - diers, For the fight to - day; Lift on high your ban - ner,
sol - diers, Vic - to - ry to win; For - ward, then, ye peo - ple,
rag - es, Vic - t'ry is at hand; See! our line ad - vanc - es,

Firmly march and true; In this fight your Leader must de-pend on you.
Forward, Church of God; See the crim-son footsteps, Where your Master trod.
Hear the shout of praise! Vict'ry crowns our banners, Loud your voices raise.

D.S. Come without delay; Arm you, Christian soldiers, For the fight to - day.

CHORUS. Call - - ing,

Hear the bu - gle call-ing, call-ing you and me; To arms! ye sol - diers

Call - - ing, D. S.

of the cross; Hear the bu - gle call-ing, call-ing you and me;

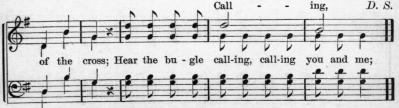

Softly and Tenderly.

W. L. T.　　　　　　　　　　　　　　　　　　WILL L. THOMPSON.

Very slow. pp

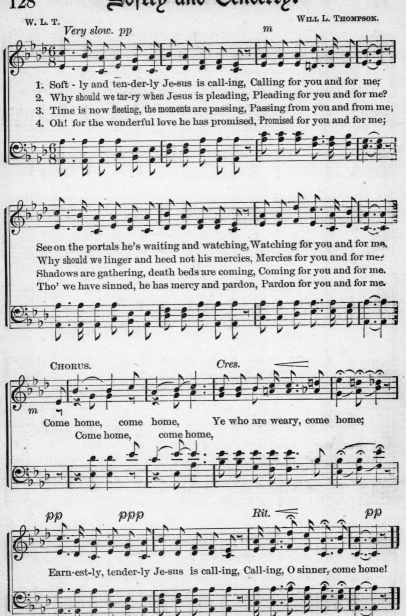

1. Soft - ly and ten-der-ly Je-sus is call-ing, Calling for you and for me;
2. Why should we tar-ry when Jesus is pleading, Pleading for you and for me?
3. Time is now fleeting, the moments are passing, Passing from you and from me;
4. Oh! for the wonderful love he has promised, Promised for you and for me;

See on the portals he's waiting and watching, Watching for you and for me.
Why should we linger and heed not his mercies, Mercies for you and for me?
Shadows are gathering, death beds are coming, Coming for you and for me.
Tho' we have sinned, he has mercy and pardon, Pardon for you and for me.

CHORUS.　　　　　　　　　　　　Cres.

Come home,　come home,　　Ye who are weary, come home;
Come home,　　come home,

pp　　　ppp　　　　　　　Rit.　　　pp

Earn-est-ly, tender-ly Je-sus is call-ing, Call-ing, O sinner, come home!

BY PER. OF WILL L. THOMPSON, EAST LIVERPOOL, O.

129 Keep your Covenant with Jesus.

MARTHA C. OLIVER. W. H. DOANE.

1. Keep your cov - e - nant with Je - sus, 'Tis the least that you can do;
2. Tho' we give our dear-est treas-ure, 'Tis a tri - fle we be-stow;
3. What are all our cares and burdens? They are shad-ows dim - ly cast;

For he died for your sal-va - tion, And he al - ways has been true.
Tho' we mete with larg-est meas-ure, 'Tis but lit - tle we can show;
They will fade and quickly van - ish, If we hold our prom-ise fast.

He has been your guide and help-er, He has been a faith-ful friend,
But he sees the good in - ten-tion And the loy - al, lov - ing will,
We can smile at all our loss - es, We can wel-come toil and pain;

And you nev - er can re - pay him, Tho' you serve him to the end.
And by giv - ing him our ut-most, We may each his charge ful - fill.
If we keep our pledge to Je - sus, None of these will be in vain.

REFRAIN.

Keep your cov - e - nant with Je - sus, To your pledge be ev - er true,

Keep your Covenant with Jesus.

For he gave him-self your ran-som; Yes, he died, he died for you.

130 We'll Win the Day.

Mrs. Harriet E. Jones.

Frank M. Davis.

1. We are com-ing! we are com-ing! From the east and from the west;
2. We are com-ing! we are com-ing! With his ban - ner float-ing high;
3. We are com-ing! we are com-ing! With the gos - pel ar - mor on;
4. We are com-ing! we are com-ing! Precious Christ, our joy and song;

On -ward, sol-diers, stand for Je - sus, Fight for him you love the best.
From the north and south we're coming, Him to serve un - til we die.
Great in num-ber, bound to con-quer In the name of God's own Son.
As we march we'll gath-er tro-phies, All the earth - ly way a - long.

Chorus.

We are com - ing! we are com-ing! Ea - ger now to join the fray;

With the Sav - ior as our Cap-tain, We will sure - ly win the day.

131 It Just Suits Me.

E. E. Hewitt.

Wm. J. Kirkpatrick.

1. What a won-der-ful sal-va-tion! For its length and breadth and height
2. Oh, this bless-ed "who-so-ev-er," Call-ing ev-'ry one who will,
3. Pre-cious prom-is-es of Je-sus, Sweeping ev-'ry hu-man need!
4. What a per-fect, pres-ent Sav-ior! What a true and lov-ing friend!

Far ex-cel the grandest knowledge Of the ser-a-phim in light;
To the sparkling, liv-ing wa-ters, Flowing ful-ly, free-ly still;
For the grace of our Re-deem-er Must our high-est tho't ex-ceed;
Can we ev-er praise him right-ly? Tell how grace and glo-ry blend?

I can nev-er, nev-er fath-om Half its ho-ly mys-ter-y,
No, I know not why he loves me, But his blood is all my plea;
To the might-y roy-al storehouse Let me use the gold-en key,
Now the Prince of Peace is reign-ing, O-ver-rul-ing all I see;

CHORUS.

But I know it is for sin-ners, And it just suits me.
I can trust his "who-so-ev-er," For it just suits me.
Find the spe-cial, ten-der prom-ise That will just suit me.
So, what-ev-er lot he or-ders, May it just suit me.

} It just suits

me, It just suits me, This won-der-ful sal-va-tion, It just suits me.

132 Have you Told it All to Jesus?

J. E. RANKIN, D. D.

J. H. TENNEY.

1. Have you told it all to Je-sus, All your weakness and your sin?
2. Have you told it all to Je-sus, Hidden in his riv-en side,
3. Have you told it all to Je-sus? Has he an-swered o'er and o'er,

Have you made a full con-fes-sion, Noth-ing left concealed with-in?
There made free and full con-fes-sion, Washed you in the crim-son tide?
"Go in peace, thou art for-giv-en, Go in peace, and sin no more!"

Have you told it all to Je-sus, Who was once for sin-ners slain?
Are you on the Rock of A-ges, And tho' bil-lows round you roll,
In the se-cret of his presence, 'Neath the shad-ow of his wing,

Have you felt the blood of cleansing, Wash-ing out your ev-'ry stain?
Do you know the joy of par-don? Is there peace with-in your soul?
Can you bid your foes de-fi-ance? Can you full sal-va-tion sing?

D. S.—Tho' they were as red as crim-son, He has washed them white as snow.

CHORUS.

D. S.

Yes, I've told it all to Je-sus, Told him all the sins I know;

133 I'm So Glad.

L. E. JONES.   W. A. OGDEN.

1. I'm glad that the Sav - ior re - deemed me, My life is all
2. I'm glad that the Sav - ior has called me From out the dark
3. I'm glad that when shad - ows hang o'er me, That in the great

sun - shine to - day; For Je - sus in won - der - ful mer - cy,
val - ley of sin; So glad that he purchas'd my par - don,
Rock I can hide; 'Twas cleft for the rest of the wea - ry;

CHORUS.

Has car - ried my sor - rows a - way.
And wel - comed the wan - der - er in.   I'm so glad!
And there I can safe - ly a - bide.

I'm so glad That who - ev - er will may be free!
                                                          be free!

I'm so glad! I'm so glad That grace reaches e-ven to me.

134 Jesus of Nazareth Passeth By.

Miss Etta Campbell.　　　　Mark x. 47.　　　　T. E. Perkins.

1. What means this ea - ger, anxious throng, Which moves with bus - y haste a - long—
2. Who is this Je - sus? Why should he The cit - y move so might-i - ly?
3. Je - sus! 'tis he who once be - low Man's pathway trod, 'mid pain and woe;
4. A - gain he comes! from place to place His ho - ly footprints we can trace.

These wondrous gath'rings day by day? What means this strange commotion, pray?
A pass-ing stran - ger, has he skill To move the mul - ti - tude at will?
And burdened ones, wher-e'er he came, Brought out their sick, and deaf, and lame.
He paus- eth at our threshold—nay, He en - ters—con-de-scends to stay.

In ac-cents hushed the throng re-ply: "Je - sus of Naz-a-reth pass-eth by,"
A - gain the stir-ring notes re-ply: "Je - sus of Naz-a-reth pass-eth by,"
The blind re-joiced to hear the cry: "Je - sus of Naz-a-reth pass-eth by,"
Shall we not glad - ly raise the cry—"Je - sus of Naz-a-reth pass-eth by,"

In ac-cents hushed the throng re-ply: "Je - sus of Naz-a-reth pass- eth by."
A - gain the stir-ring notes re- ply: "Je - sus of Naz-a-reth pass- eth by."
The blind re-joiced to hear the cry: "Je - sus of Naz-a-reth pass- eth by."
Shall we not glad - ly raise the cry—"Je - sus of Naz-a-reth pass- eth by."

5 Ho! all ye heavy-laden, come!
　Here's pardon, comfort, rest, and home!
　Ye wanderers from a Father's face!
　Return, accept his proffered grace.
　Ye tempted ones, there's refuge nigh:
　"Jesus of Nazareth passeth by."

6 But if you still this call refuse,
　And all his wondrous love abuse,
　Soon will he sadly from you turn,
　Your bitter prayer for pardon spurn.
　"Too late! too late!" will be the cry—
　"Jesus of Nazareth has passed by."

135 Wonderful Story of Love.

J. M. D

Rev. J. M. DRIVER.

1. Won-der-ful sto-ry of love: Tell it to me a-gain; Wonderful
2. Won-der-ful sto-ry of love: Tho' you are far a-way; Wonderful
3. Won-der-ful sto-ry of love: Je-sus provides a rest; Wonderful

sto-ry of love: Wake the im-mor-tal strain! An-gels with rap-ture an-
sto-ry of love: Still he doth call to-day; Call-ing from Cal-va-ry's
sto-ry of love: For all the pure and blest; Rest in those mansions a-

nounce it, Shepherds with wonder receive it; Sinner, oh! won't you believe it?
mountain, Down from the crystal bright fountain, E'en from the dawn of creation,
bove us, With those who've gone on before us, Singing the rapturous cho-rus,

CHORUS.

Wonderful sto-ry of love. Won - der - ful! Won -
Wonderful sto-ry of love; Wonderful

der - ful! Won - der - ful! Wonderful sto-ry of love!
sto-ry of love: Wonderful story of love:

Cleanse and Fill Me.

ABBIE MILLS.

Dr. H. L. GILMOUR.

1. I am com-ing, Je - sus, com-ing, At thy feet I hum-bly bow;
2. Take a - way the bent to sin-ning, Ev -'ry bit - ter root with in;
3. Search as with a light-ed can - dle Ev -'ry hid - den cor - ner, Lord;
4. Now thou art the blood ap - ply - ing, I am clean, I feel the flow
5. Lo! the prom-ise of the Fa - ther Swift descends, and fills me now;

I have tast - ed thy sal - va - tion, But I want the full-ness now.
Heal the tide at its be - gin-ning, That has caused me oft to sin.
Sep - a - rate me from the e - vil Thro' thine ev - er - liv - ing Word.
That a - lone hath power to make me Whit - er than the pur - est snow.
Glo - ry, glo - ry, hal - le - lu - jah! Thou art cleans-ing, fill - ing now.

CHORUS.

Cleanse and fill me, cleanse and fill me, Fill me with thy Spir - it now;
5th v. Cleansing, filling, cleansing, fill-ing, Thou art cleans-ing, fill - ing now;

Cleanse and fill me, bless-ed Je - sus, Fill me with thy Spir - it now.
Glo - ry, glo - ry, hal - le - lu - jah! Thou art cleansing, fill - ing now

137 May the Master Count on You?

E. A. H.

Rev. Elisha A. Hoffman.

1. When the trum-pet sounds to bat - tle with the strong and wi - ly foe,
2. There are those who fol - low Je - sus when there is no cross to bear,
3. Are you ful - ly con - se - crat - ed to the serv - ice of the Lord?

And the hosts of our Im-man-uel to the earn-est con-flict go,
But re - fuse the bur-den-bear-ing and the toils with him to share;
Are you read - y on the bat - tle-field to wield for him the sword?

Will you prove that you are loy - al? Will you prove that you are true?
Oh! it grieves the bless-ed Mas-ter that their hearts are so un-true;
Are you one a-mong the faith-ful? Are you one a-mong the true?

FINE.

For de - vot - ed, faith-ful serv-ice may the Mas-ter count on you?
Sure - ly for a bet - ter serv-ice the dear Lord may count on you?
And for stead-y, life-long serv-ice may the Mas-ter count on you?

D. S. In the thick-est of the bat - tle, To be faith-ful, to be true?

CHORUS.

D. S.

May he count on you, my broth-er? May the Mas - ter count on you,

Christ is All.

W. A. W.

W. A. WILLIAMS.

May be sung as a Solo and Chorus.

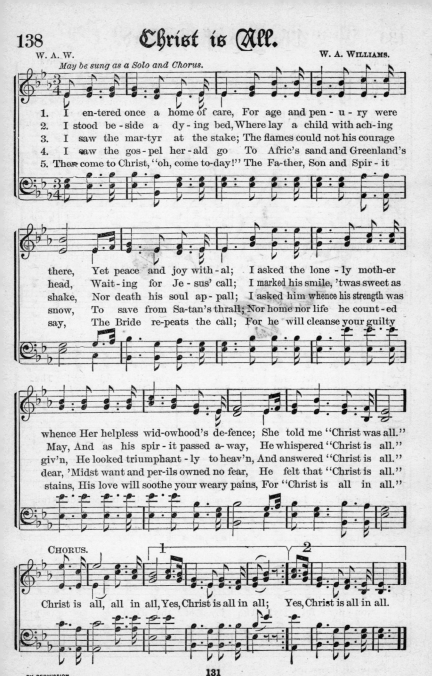

1. I en-tered once a home of care, For age and pen - u - ry were
2. I stood be - side a dy - ing bed, Where lay a child with ach - ing
3. I saw the mar-tyr at the stake; The flames could not his courage
4. I saw the gos - pel her - ald go To Afric's sand and Greenland's
5. Then come to Christ, "oh, come to-day!" The Fa-ther, Son and Spir - it

there, Yet peace and joy with - al; I asked the lone - ly moth-er
head, Wait-ing for Je - sus' call; I marked his smile, 'twas sweet as
shake, Nor death his soul ap - pall; I asked him whence his strength was
snow, To save from Sa-tan's thrall; Nor home nor life he count-ed
say, The Bride re-peats the call; For he will cleanse your guilty

whence Her helpless wid-ow-hood's de-fence; She told me "Christ was all."
May, And as his spir - it passed a- way, He whispered "Christ is all."
giv'n, He looked triumphant - ly to heav'n, And answered "Christ is all."
dear, 'Midst want and per-ils owned no fear, He felt that "Christ is all."
stains, His love will soothe your weary pains, For "Christ is all in all."

CHORUS.

Christ is all, all in all, Yes, Christ is all in all; Yes, Christ is all in all.

139 The Joy of the Lord.

L. W. S.   LANTA WILSON SMITH.

1. The joy of the Lord is my strength; My courage and hope to re - new,
2. The joy of the Lord is my strength; In sor-row and tri-al, how sweet;
3. The joy of the Lord is my strength; The pleasures this world can be-stow

As forth to the con - flict I go, The strong-holds of sin to sub - due.
A sol - ace that nev - er can fail, A com - fort di - vine and com - plete.
No long - er can charm or al - lure, While life with this joy is a - glow.

CHORUS.

Oh, won - der - ful joy, wonder - ful joy! The
Oh, won - der - ful, won - der - ful, won - der - ful joy!

joy of the Lord is my strength, Oh, won - der - ful, won - der - ful,

won - der - ful joy! The joy of the Lord is my strength.

140 Jesus Saves.

PRISCILLA J. OWENS.   WM. J. KIRKPATRICK.

1. We have heard a joy-ful sound, Je-sus saves, Je-sus saves;
2. Waft it on the roll-ing tide, Je-sus saves, Je-sus saves;
3. Sing a-bove the bat-tle's strife, Je-sus saves, Je-sus saves;
4. Give the winds a might-y voice, Je-sus saves, Je-sus saves;

Spread the glad-ness all a-round, Je-sus saves, Je-sus saves;
Tell to sin-ners, far and wide, Je-sus saves, Je-sus saves;
By his death and end-less life, Je-sus saves, Je-sus saves;
Let the na-tions now re-joice, Je-sus saves, Je-sus saves;

Bear the news to ev'-ry land, Climb the steeps and cross the waves,
Sing, ye is-lands of the sea, Ech-o back, ye o-cean caves,
Sing it soft-ly thro' the gloom, When the heart for mer-cy craves,
Shout sal-va-tion full and free, High-est hills and deep-est caves,

On-ward, 'tis our Lord's com-mand, Je-sus saves, Je-sus saves.
Earth shall keep her ju-bi-lee, Je-sus saves, Je-sus saves.
Sing in tri-umph o'er the tomb, Je-sus saves, Je-sus saves.
This our song of vic-to-ry, Je-sus saves, Je-sus saves.

141 God is Calling Yet.

GERHARD TERSTEEGEN.

E. O. EXCELL.

1. God calling yet! shall I not hear? Earth's pleasures shall I still hold dear?
2. God calling yet! shall I not rise? Can I his lov-ing voice de-spise,
3. God calling yet! and shall he knock, And I my heart the clos-er lock?
4. God calling yet! and shall I give No heed, but still in bondage live?
5. God calling yet! I can not stay; My heart I yield without de-lay:

Shall life's swift passing years all fly, And still my soul in slumber lie?
And base-ly his kind care re-pay? He calls me still; can I de-lay?
He still is wait-ing to re-ceiv- And shall I dare his Spir-it grieve?
I wait, but he does not for-sake; He calls me still; my heart, a-wake!
Vain world, farewell, from thee I part; The voice of God has reach'd my heart.

CHORUS.

Call - - - ing, oh, hear him, Call - - - ing, oh, hear him, God is
God is calling yet, God is call-ing yet,

call - ing yet, oh, hear him calling, call-ing, Call - - - ing, oh, hear him,
God is call-ing yet,

Call - - - ing, oh, hear him, God is calling yet, oh, hear him calling yet.
God is calling yet,

142 Oh, such Wonderful Love!

I. N. McHose. Alt.

I. N. McHose.

1. O the great love the dear Sav-ior has shown To shame-ful-ly
2. Pal - ac - es, man-sions and inns had no room For Christ, who so
3. Man of great sor - rows and homeless was he, But yet my Re-

die on the tree, Leav-ing his scep-tre and beau - ti - ful throne
joy - ful - ly came Down from yon heav-en our path to il - lume,
deem-er and Friend, Pour-ing in in - fi-nite streams up - on me,

CHORUS.

To res - cue a sin - ner like me! Oh,...... ...... such
And save us from sin and from shame.
A love that can nev - er-more end. Oh, such won-der - ful,

won-der - ful love! Oh,...... such won-der-ful love! Je - sus, my
Oh, such wonderful,

Sav-ior, left scep-tre and throne, To res-cue a sin-ner like me.

143 Wonderful Army of God.

W. A. S.

W. A. SPENCER, D. D.

1. There's a won-der-ful arm-y now march-ing, But its war-fare is
2. Float-ing out o'er this won-der-ful arm-y Is the ban-ner of
3. There's a place in this won-der-ful arm-y For the loy-al, true-
4. All the arm-ies of e-vil must per-ish, But the glo-ri-ous
5. Then all hail to the con-quer-ing Chief-tian, Who is vic-tor o'er

not one of blood; For by mer-cy and love are the con-quest Of the
in- fi-nite love; While the songs of earth's con-quer-ing le-gions Ech-o
heart-ed and brave, Who will fol-low the bless-ed Re-deem-er Fol-low
prom-ise is giv'n, That our arm-y, in youth ev-er-last-ing, Shall as-
death and the grave; Swift to res-cue the world's dark-est province March-es

CHORUS.

won-der-ful arm-y of God. }
back from the arm-ies a-bove. }
Je-sus the might-y to save. } Who will march in this won-der-ful
sem-ble un-bro-ken in heav'n. }
Je-sus the might-y to save. }

arm-y, With the ban-ner of Je-sus un-furled? Who will march in this

won-der-ful arm-y, March-ing with Je-sus to con-quer the world?

144 Why Are You Waiting.

E. A. H.

Rev. Elisha A. Hoffman.

1. Why are you wait-ing, broth-er? Why do you still de-lay?
2. Why are you wait-ing, broth-er? Why is your heart so cold?
3. Why are you wait-ing, broth-er? Why still un-rec-on-ciled?
4. Why are you wait-ing, broth-er? Je-sus is ver-y near,

En-ter the door of mer-cy; Come, and be saved to-day.
Why not re-turn, re-pent-ant, In-to the Sav-ior's fold?
This is God's time of mer-cy; Trust him, and be his child.
Bless-ing and sav-ing oth-ers, Read-y to save you here.

Chorus.

Why are you waiting? Why are you waiting? Now is God's gra-cious hour!

Why are you waiting? Why are you waiting? Now he will save with power.

145 What Hast Thou Done For Me?

Key C.

1 I gave my life for thee,
　My precious blood I shed
That thou might'st ransomed be,
　And quickened from the dead.
‖: I gave, I gave my life for thee, :‖
　What hast thou given for me?

2 My Father's house of light,
　My glory-circled throne
I left, for earthly night,
　For wand'rings sad and lone.
‖: I left, I left it all for thee,
　Hast thou left aught for me?

3 I suffered much for thee,
　More than thy tongue can tell,
Of bitterest agony,
　To rescue thee from hell;
‖: I've borne, I've borne it all for thee, :‖
　What hast thou borne for me?

4 And I have brought to thee,
　Down from my home above,
Salvation full and free,
　My pardon and my love;
‖: I bring, I bring rich gifts to thee, :‖
　What hast thou brought to me?

F. R. Havergal.

146. The Bondage of Love.

George D. Watson.　　　Joseph Garrison.

1. O sweet will of God! thou hast girded me round, Like the deep, moving
   With omnip-o-tent love is my poor nature bound, And this bondage to

2. For years my soul wrestled with vague dis-con-tent, That like a sad
   God's light in my soul with the darkness was blent, And my heart ev-er

3. And now I have flung my-self reckless-ly out, Like a chip on the
   I pass the rough rocks with a smile and a shout, And I just let my

CHORUS.

currents that gird-le the sea;
love sets me per-fect-ly free.
an-gel o'er-shadowed my way;
longed for an un-cloud-ed day.
stream of the In-fin-ite Will;
God his dear pur-pose ful-fill.

Hal-le-lu-jah! hal-le-lu-jah! my

soul is now free! For the precious blood of Je-sus cleanseth e-ven me.

4 Forever I choose the good will of my God,
　Its holy deep riches to love and to know,
The serfdom of love to so sweeten the rod,
　That its touch maketh rivers of honey to flow.

5 Roll on, checkered seasons, bring smiles or bring tears,
My soul sweetly sails on an infinite tide;
I shall soon touch the shores of eternity's years,
　And near the white throne of my Savior abide.

147. His Yoke is Easy.

Ps. XXIII.　　　R. E. Hudson.

1. The Lord is my Shepherd, I shall not want, He mak-eth me down to
2. My soul cri-eth out: "re-store me a-gain, And give me the strength to
3. Yea, tho' I should walk in the val-ley of death, Yet why should I fear from

His Yoke is Easy.

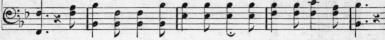

lie   In pastures green, he lead-eth me The qui-et wa-ters by.
take The nar-row path of righteous-ness, E'en for his own name's sake."
ill? For thou art with me, and thy rod And staff me comfort still.

CHORUS.

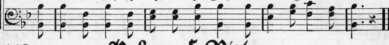

His yoke is eas-y, his burden is light, I've found it so, I've found it so.

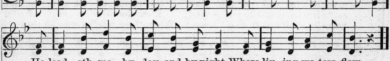

He lead-eth me, by day and by night, Where liv-ing wa-ters flow.

148 Palms of Victory.

R. KELSO CARTER.   Arranged.

CHORUS.

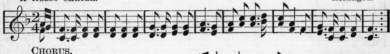

Then palms of vic-to-ry, crowns of glory, Palms of vic-to-ry I shall wear.

1 I saw a blood-washed pilgrim,
    A sinner saved by grace,
Upon the King's great highway,
    With peaceful, shining face.
Temptations sore beset him,
    But nothing could affright,
He said, "The yoke is easy,
    The burden, it is light."—CHO.

2 I saw him in the furnace,
    He doubted not, nor feared,
And in the flames beside him
    The Son of God appeared.
Though seven times 'twas heated
    With all the tempter's might,
He said, "The yoke is easy,
    The burden, it is light."—CHO.

3 Mid storms, and clouds, and trials,
    In prison, at the stake,
He leaped for joy, rejoicing,
    'Twas all for Jesus' sake.
That God should count him worthy,
    Was such supreme delight,
He cried, "The yoke is easy,
    The burden is so light."—CHO

4 I saw him overcoming,
    Through all the swelling strife,
Until he crossed the threshold
    Of God's Eternal Life.
The Crown, the Throne, the Sceptre
    The Name, the Stone so White,
Were his, who found, in Jesus,
    The yoke and burden light.—CHO.

149 The Master Wants Workers.

Rev. F. J. STEVENS. J. H. HALL.

1. The Mas - ter wants work - ers, his har - vest is white, His com-
2. The Mas - ter wants work - ers, and that which is right He will
3. The Mas - ter wants work - ers, each serv - ice he knows, Not a
4. The Mas - ter wants work - ers, the night com - eth soon, When the

mand, "Go ye forth," is to all; Go work with a will, and let
give at the end of the day; So thrust in the sick - le and
serv - ice too small to re - cord; E'en he who a cup of cold
wea - ry shall rest from all care; When those who have toil'd thro' the

not the dark night On an un - gath - ered har - vest - field fall.
work with thy might: If not gath - ered ripe grain will de - cay.
wa - ter be - stows "In his name" shall not lose his re - ward.
heat of the noon Shall no long - er its wea - ri - ness bear.

CHORUS.

The Mas - - - ter wants work - - ers, a host.........
The Mas - ter wants workers, and call - eth a - gain, The Master wants work-

of true men,............ To gath - - er the
ers, a host of true men, To gath - er the lost ones from

151 There is a Home.

ELISHA A. HOFFMAN.   W. A. OGDEN.

1. There is a home, a bless-ed home, In that fair land a-bove,
2. There is a home, a heav'n-ly home, In fade-less ver-dure drest,
3. There is a home, a hap-py home, Where care and sorrow cease,

Where peace and hap-pi-ness a-bound,—The Par-a-dise of Love.
Where toil and la-bor are no more,—The Par-a-dise of Rest.
Where sin and sick-ness nev-er come,—The Par-a-dise of Peace.

REFRAIN.

This bless-ed home............ our gra-cious Lord..... Has
This bless-ed home our gra-cious Lord, our Lord

pur-chas'd with his blood, That we might en - - - - - ter,
That we might en-ter,

thro' the gates,.. ..... The Par-a-dise of God.
thro' its gates, its gates,

152 Leave it All with Jesus.

IDA SCOTT TAYLOR.

W. E. PENN.

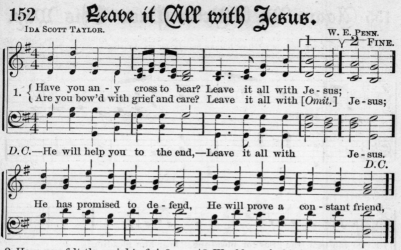

1. { Have you an-y cross to bear? Leave it all with Je-sus;
   { Are you bow'd with grief and care? Leave it all with [Omit.] Je-sus;

D.C.—He will help you to the end,—Leave it all with Je-sus.

He has promised to de-fend, He will prove a con-stant friend,

2 Have you felt the weight of sin?
   Leave it all with Jesus;
He will make you clean within—
   Leave it all with Jesus;
In the sacred healing flow,
He will wash you white as snow
If you humbly, trusting go;—
   Leave it all with Jesus.

3 Would you in his image live?
   Leave it all with Jesus;
He can every blessing give,—
   Leave it all with Jesus;
He will lead you safely through,
He is merciful and true,
He has died for love of you—
   Leave it all with Jesus.

153 Workman of God!

F. W. FABER.

Tune: ARLINGTON. C. M.

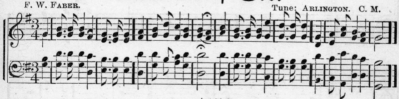

1 Workman of God! O lose not heart,
   But learn what God is like;
And in the darkest battle-field
   Thou shalt know where to strike.

2 Thrice blest is he to whom is given
   The instinct that can tell
That God is on the field, when he
   Is most invisible.

3 Blest too is he who can divine
   Where real right doth lie,
And dares to take the side that seems
   Wrong to man's blind-fold eye.

4 Then learn to scorn the praise of men,
   And learn to lose with God;
For Jesus won the world thro' shame,
   And beckon's thee his road.

154 Oh, for a Faith.

1 Oh, for a faith that will not shrink,
   Though pressed by every foe,
That will not tremble on the brink
   Of any earthly woe;—

2 A faith that shines more bright and clear
   When tempests rage without;
That when in danger knows no fear,
   In darkness feels no doubt;—

3 A faith that keeps the narrow way
   Till life's last hour has fled,
And with a pure and heavenly ray
   Illumes a dying bed.

4 Lord, give us such a faith as this,
   And then, whate'er may come,
We'll taste, e'en here, the hallowed bliss
   Of an eternal home.

W. H. BATHURST.

155 Again We'll Never Pass This Way.

"I expect to pass this way but once; if, therefore, there be any kindness I can show, or any good thing I can do to my fellow human beings, let me do it now; let me not defer nor neglect it, for I shall not pass this way again."

P. H. Bristow.

W. A. Ogden.

Andante.

Solo.

1. Do you hear the Sav-ior plead-ing, hear him pleading?
2. Out up-on the mountains drear-y, cold and dreary,
3. Ev-'ry day some soul is dy - ing, yes, is dy-ing,

pp Quartet.

hear him pleading?
cold and drear-y,
yes, is dy - ing,

"Go ye forth in - to my vine - yard day by day;
There are souls that may be wait - ing just for you;
On the mountains where they lin - ger, far a - way,

pp Quartet.

day by day;
just for you;
far a - way,

Again We'll Never Pass This Way.

Go ye forth, I will be with you in-ter-ced-ing, (in-ter-ced-ing,)
May be wait-ing near your pathway, oh, so wea-ry; (oh, so wea-ry;)
While the Mas-ter on yourself may be re-ly-ing, (be re-ly-ing,)

That some soul may from the dark-ness turn a-way." (turn a-way.")
Will you not go out and tell them God is true? (God is true?)
That he gets the in-vi-ta-tion while 'tis day. (while 'tis day.)

Chorus. *Response. Allegro.*

We will go and God be with us, with us ev-er; We will

take the words of Je-sus as our stay; And to lift a fall-en brother

we'll en-deav-or, For we know we ne'er again may pass this way, (this way.)

145

156 Save Some One To-day.

L. W. S.　　　　　　　　　　　　　　　　　　LANTA WILSON SMITH.

1. Countless the per-ils that threaten to-day, Dan-gers are wait-ing each
2. Are we neg-lect-ing the words we should say, Words that might save a poor
3. Are we in safe-ty and those that we love All on the way to the

step of the way; Ma - ny now care - less are meet-ing their doom; O
sin - ner to - day? Why are we care-less when no one can know The
heav - en a - bove? O then in pit - y reach out to the lost, To-

CHORUS.

what is more cer-tain than death and the tomb?)
fate that a day or an hour may be-stow? } Moments are fly-ing,
day haste to save them at what-ev - er cost.)

Sin-ners are dy-ing, Shall we save some one to - day?.... Mo-ments are
to - day?

fly-ing, Sin-ners are dy-ing, We must save some one to - day.........
save some one to-day.

On the Jericho Road.

Dr. J. J. Maxfield.

W. A. Ogden.

1. On the Jer-i-cho road there is serv-ice to-day, For all who are
2. On the Jer-i-cho road you will find him to-day, Your brother who
3. On the Jer-i-cho road ma-ny forc-es combine, To sti-fle the

read-y to work or to pray, A-round us are ly-ing the
wan-ders from Je-sus a-way, Oh, wait not to-mor-row, his
voice of the Spir-it Di-vine, A-bout us are ly-ing the

wounded and dy-ing, And few the Sa-mar-i-tans pass-ing that way.
deep cup of sor-row Is brimming and bit-ter, no long-er de-lay.
wounded and dy-ing, Go, broth-er, and pour in the oil and the wine.

CHORUS.

On the Jer-i-cho road, leading down, The Levite goes carelessly by,
down, down, down,

Yet ma-ny who journey a-long that way, Are wounded and ready to die.

158 Suffer the Children to Come.

Dr. I. L. MITCHELL.

W. A. OGDEN.

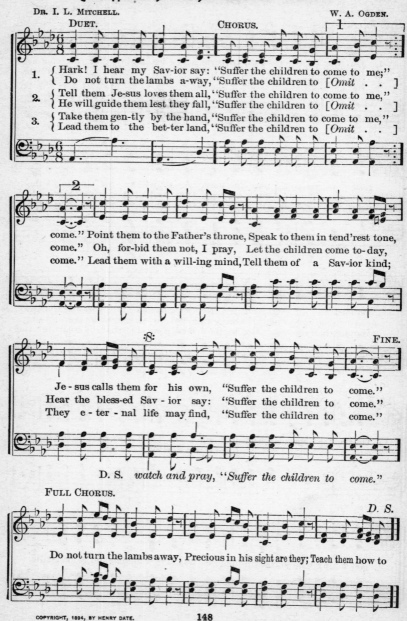

1. { Hark! I hear my Sav-ior say: "Suffer the children to come to me;"
   { Do not turn the lambs a-way, "Suffer the children to [*Omit* . .]

2. { Tell them Je-sus loves them all, "Suffer the children to come to me,"
   { He will guide them lest they fall, "Suffer the children to [*Omit* . .]

3. { Take them gen-tly by the hand, "Suffer the children to come to me,"
   { Lead them to the bet-ter land, "Suffer the children to [*Omit* . .]

come." Point them to the Father's throne, Speak to them in tend'rest tone,
come." Oh, for-bid them not, I pray, Let the children come to-day,
come." Lead them with a will-ing mind, Tell them of a Sav-ior kind;

Je-sus calls them for his own, "Suffer the children to come."
Hear the bless-ed Sav-ior say: "Suffer the children to come."
They e-ter-nal life may find, "Suffer the children to come."

D. S. *watch and pray,* "*Suffer the children to come.*"

FULL CHORUS.

Do not turn the lambs away, Precious in his sight are they; Teach them how to

148

159

He Keepeth Me, Ever.

E. R. Latta.

Geo. F. Rosche.

1. He keep-eth me, ev - er, Wher - e'er be the place! I've on - ly to
2. He keep-eth me, ev - er, With ten-der-est care! I've on - ly to
3. He keep-eth me, ev - er, From yielding to dread, Tho' darkness be

ask it—Most won-der-ful grace! Though sor - est temp-ta - tions
ask him My bur-dens to bear! A word of his prom - ise
round me, And clouds o - ver - head! He still - eth my doubtings,

My spir - it may try, I know my Re - deem - er
He nev - er will break! Who - ev - er may leave me,
He light - ens my grief! I've on - ly to trust him—

CHORUS.

Will ev - er be nigh!
He ne'er will for - sake! } He keepeth me, ev - er! His love end-eth
He'll give me re - lief!

nev - er! From Him, naught shall sev-er! He keep-eth my soul!

160   I Am Now a Child of God.

M. L. McPhail.   M. L. McPhail.

1. I am now a child of God, thro' the all - a - ton-ing blood That was
2. How I glo - ry in the tho't—that the precious blood hath brought Hope of
3. I'm re-joic-ing all the day, since my Sav-ior rolled a - way All the

shed up - on the cross of Cal-va-ry; 'Twas the price that Je-sus paid for my
ev - er-last-ing life to all the race; In his loving heart there's room for the
weight of sin that pressed my weary soul; I will of - fer heart-felt praise to his

sins on him were laid, And I now thro' him am made for - ev - er free.
poor - est that will come; For within His love I found my rest-ing place.
name thro' all the days, As I press my jour-ney on-ward to the goal.

CHORUS.

What won - drous love! what match - less love! The
What wondrous love!   what matchless love.

Fa - ther hath be-stowed;   He gave   His Son that
The Fa - ther hath bestowed, he hath be-stowed; He gave his Son

I Am Now a Child of God.

Rit.

I might be a child, a child of God.
that I might be a child, a child of God, of God.

161 Jesus is Able to Save.

ELISHA A. HOFFMAN.

W. A. OGDEN.

1. We glo-ri-fy God for the gift of his Son, And for the great
2. The mo-ment a sin-ner on Je-sus be-lieves,That mo-ment a
3. O won-drous re-demp-tion, the pur-chase of blood,—Secured thro' the

work the Re-deem-er has done! Him-self as a ran-som he will-ing-ly
par-don for sin he re-ceives; No sin-ner in vain his forgiv'ness shall
death of the dear Son of God! His life as a ran-som for sin-ners He

CHORUS.

gave, And he is a-bund-ant-ly a-ble to save.)
crave, For he is a-bund-ant-ly a-ble to save. } Oh, tell the glad news,
gave, Yes, he is a-bund-ant-ly a-ble to save.)

Go spread it a-far, That Je-sus is a-ble and will-ing to save.

162 Behold, the Bridegroom Comes.

J. M. W.   J. M. WHYTE.

1. We shall hear a voice, an im-mor-tal voice, "Behold, the Bridegroom
2. When the voice shall cry, "Go ye forth to-night, Behold, the Bridegroom
3. Broth-er, trim your lamp, have it burning bright, "Behold, the Bridegroom
4. Hast thou made a vow? hast-en ye to pay, "Behold, the Bridegroom

comes!" At the mid-night watch, in the dark-ness deep,
comes!" Then the pulse will cease, and the heart grow still,
comes!" He will sure-ly come, though he seem-eth late,
comes!" For when he has come, and hath closed the door,

When a-cross our souls heav-y slum-bers creep, We shall
And the eyes will close, and the blood grow chill, And the
Be at peace with him, nor a mo-ment wait, You will
And ye stand and pray, "O-pen, we im-plore," It will

hear that voice, that im-mor-tal voice, "Behold, the Bridegroom comes!"
soul will take its e-ter-nal flight, "For lo, the Bridegroom comes!"
hear the cry ere the morn-ing light, "Behold, the Bridegroom comes!"
be too late,—pay thy vows to-day, "Behold, the Bridegroom comes!"

CHORUS.

Oh, be read-y when the Bridegroom comes! Oh, be read-y when the

Behold, the Bridegroom Comes.

Bridegroom comes! At the noon-tide, In the evening, At the
He comes, He comes, He

mid-night, in the morn - - - - ing, Oh, be read - y,
comes, in the morn-ing, Oh, be read - y, He

Oh, be read - y, Oh, be read - y when the Bride-groom comes!
comes, He comes, be read - y when the Bride-groom comes!

163 Death and Eternity.

C. H. G.

CHAS. H. GABRIEL.

Feelingly.

1. Com-ing when the day is bright, Com-ing in the si - lent night,
2. Com-ing to the gay and proud, Com-ing with a snow-white shroud,
3. Com-ing with un - hin - dered sway, Com-ing ev - 'ry fleet - ing day,
4. Com-ing to the sin - ful one, Com-ing when our life is done,

Slow ad lib. *Echo.*

Coming at the morning light,
Coming to the gray head bowed,
Coming to the young and gay,
Gath'ring to the judgment throne,
Coming, coming, death and e-ter-ni-ty, e-ter-ni-ty.

164 Children of the King.

LANTA WILSON SMITH. W. A. OGDEN.

1. Oh, how beau - ti - ful the com-ing Of the her - alds of the King, As the mes - sage of sal - va - tion To the lost they glad - ly bring. Speed ye chil - - dren of the King, Let the bless - - ed ti - dings ring; Till from ev - 'ry land shall ech - o: "We are chil - dren of the King."

2. You shall res - cue souls from dan-ger As the sto - ry you re-peat, And in place of sin and dark - ness Leave a joy and bliss com-plete. Speed ye chil - dren of the King, the king, Let the bless - ed ti - dings ring;

3. Speed a - way o'er hill and val - ley Like a bird on tire - less wing, Fill the air with songs of glo - ry Till the world for joy shall sing.

INST.

CHORUS.

165

Launch Out.

A. B. Simpson.

R. Kelso Carter.

1. The mer-cy of God is an o-cean di-vine, A bound-less and fath-om-less flood; Launch out in the deep, cut a- way the shore-line, And be lost in the full-ness of God.

2. But ma-ny, a-las! on-ly stand on the shore, And gaze on the o-cean so wide; They nev-er have ven-tured its depths to ex-plore, Or to launch on the fath-om-less tide.

3. And oth-ers just ven-ture a-way from the land, And lin-ger so near to the shore, That the surf and the slime that beat o-ver the strand, Dash o'er them in floods ev-er-more.

4. Oh, let us launch out on this o-cean so broad, Where the floods of sal-va-tion o'er-flow; Oh, let us be lost in the mer-cy of God, Till the depths of His full-ness we know.

CHORUS.

Launch out........ in-to the deep, Oh, let the shore-line
Oh, launch out in the deep,

go; Launch out, launch out in the o-cean divine, Out where the full tides flow.

166 In Whom I Have Redemption.

F. M. D.

FRANK M. DAVIS.

1. I know in whom I have re-demp-tion, In whom I have be-lieved,
2. I know that he who stilled the tempest Has touched my troubled heart,
3. I know that some day I shall see him In yon bright courts a-bove,

Whence com-eth peace that pass-eth knowledge, That saving grace re - ceived.
Re - newed with-in my faint-ing spir - it, And bade my fears de - part.
And bear the like-ness of my Sav - ior— Saved by re-deem-ing love.

CHORUS.

'Tis noth-ing that.......... I've done can mer - it This
'Tis noth-ing that I've done can mer - it

love that Christ.......... for me has shown;.. .... He
This love that Christ for me has shown;

sought me when.......... I was a stran - ger, In
He sought me when I was a stran-ger,

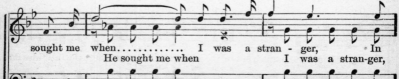

In Whom I have Redemption.

love re - deemed............ me for his own.
In love re-deemed me for his own, for his own.

167 Only a Look!

F. S. SHEPHERD.

W. A. OGDEN.

1. On - ly a look at Je - sus! O soul bow'd down with sin,
2. On - ly a look at Je - sus! O soul by care op - prest,
3. On - ly a look at Je - sus! O soul, lift up thine eyes,

A look will give sal - va - tion, E - ter - nal life will win.
A look at Christ, the Sav - ior, Will bring thee peace and rest.
For soon the Lord will hail thee From mansions in the skies.

CHORUS.

On - ly a look, on - ly a look, It is a sim - ple thing;

Yet won - der - ful the bless - ing A look in faith will bring.

168 On to Victory.

E. A. H. Rev. Elisha A. Hoffman.

1. Christian, gird the ar-mor on, There's a vic-t'ry to be won
2. Let His ban-ner be un-furled Till it waves o'er all the world,
3. When the bat-tle shall be done, And the vic-to-ry be won,
4. That will be an hour of joy, Praise shall then our tongues employ

For the Lord, for the Lord; Take the hel-met, sword and shield,
Sea to sea, shore to shore, Till the na-tions all shall own
Con-flict past, con-flict past, In the new Je-ru-sa-lem
More and more, more and more; We shall stand be-fore the King,

Forth un-to the bat-tle-field At his word, at his word.
He is King and he a-lone Ev-er-more, ev-er-more.
We shall wear a di-a-dem At the last, at the last.
And the song of tri-umph sing Ev-er-more, ev-er-more.

CHORUS.

On we'll march.... to vic-to-ry, Je-sus will our lead-er be,
On we'll march to vic-to-ry,

Je-sus will our lead-er be; On we'll march....... to vic-to-
On we'll march

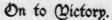

On to Victory.

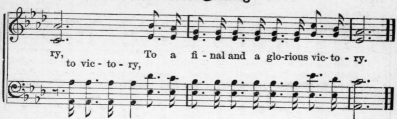

ry, To a fi-nal and a glo-rious vic-to-ry.
to vic-to-ry,

169 ## Jesus Alone Can Save.

M. L. McPhail.   M. L. McPhail.

1. No oth-er name on earth to men is given; Je-sus a-lone can save;
2. He o-pens wide the door, oh, en-ter in; Je-sus a-lone can save;
3. Rest all up-on him—do not be a-fraid;—Je-sus a-lone can save;
4. Turn ye a-way from things of earth and sin, Je-sus a-lone can save;

:S: FINE.

Where-by they can be saved, on earth or heav'n; Je-sus a-lone can save.
He is a might-y Sav-ior from all sin; Je-sus a-lone can save.
He is the sure found-a-tion God hath laid; Je-sus a-lone can save.
Trust now and ev-er-more a-lone in Him; Je-sus a-lone can save

D.S. His bless-ed kingdom shall for-ev-er stand; Je-sus a-lone can save.

CHORUS.   D. S.

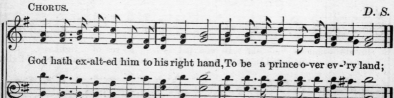

God hath ex-alt-ed him to his right hand, To be a prince o-ver ev-'ry land;

170 The Mansions Yonder.

Mrs. E. W. CHAPMAN.　　　　　　　　　　　　　　　　　　J. H. TENNEY.

1. Shall we reach the home in glo - ry When the years of life are gone?
2. Shall we see the blessed Sav - ior Ra-diant with e - ter-nal light,
3. Shall we share the joys e - ter - nal, And the glo - ry all di - vine?

Shall we sing the dear old sto - ry With redeemed ones 'round the throne?
With him dwell in heav'n for-ev - er, Clothed in robes of pur - est white?
Shall we, with the pure and ho - ly, In the heav'nly cit - y shine?

CHORUS.

Yes, we'll reach........ the man-sions yon - - der; If we
Yes, we'll reach the mansions, reach the mansions yonder,

keep....... the ar - mor bright, We will greet........ our
If we keep the armor bright, the armor bright, We will greet our

loved im-mor - - tals In yon pal - - a-ces of light.
loved immortals, loved immortals In yon pal-a-ces, yon pal-a-ces of light.

171. Jesus for Me.

W. J. K.

WM. J. KIRKPATRICK.

1. Je - sus, my Sav - ior, is all things to me; Oh, what a won-der-ful
2. Je - sus in sickness, and Je - sus in health, Je - sus in pov - er - ty,
3. He is my Ref - uge, my Rock, and my Tower, He is my For-tress, my
4. He is my Prophet, my Priest and my King, He is my Bread of Life,
5. Je - sus in sor - row, in joy, or in pain, Je - sus my Treasure in

Sav - ior is he, Guid - ing, pro-tect - ing, o'er life's roll-ing sea,
com - fort or wealth, Sun-shine or tem-pest, what-ev - er it be,
Strength and my pow'r; Life ev - er - last - ing, my Day's-man is he,
Fount-ain and Spring; Bright Sun of Right-eous-ness, Day-star is he,
loss or in gain; Con - stant Com-pan - ion, wher-e'er I may be,

CHORUS.

Might - y De - liv - 'rer— Je - sus for me.
He is my safe - ty:— Je - sus for me.
Bless - ed Re - deem-er— Je - sus for me.
Horn of Sal - va - tion— Je - sus for me.
Liv - ing or dy - ing— Je - sus for me.

Je - sus for me,

Je - sus for me, All the time ev - 'rywhere, Je - sus for me.

172 Calvary's Stream is Flowing.

ELISHA A. HOFFMAN.
Chorus by J. C. BATEMAN.

Arr. from an English Melody by
J. H. TENNEY.

1. A crim-son stream is flow-ing From rug-ged Cal-va-ry,
2. There is a stream of heal-ing Whose wa-ters clear and sweet,
3. O stream of love e-ter-nal! O source of pur-i-ty!
4. I long for per-fect cleans-ing; I long for per-fect peace;

A tide of life which cleans-es From all im-pur-i-ty;
Are for the wea-ry na-tions, Help-less at Je-sus' feet;
O grace of God a-bund-ant! O fount-ain rich and free!
I yearn to have the con-flicts With-in my spir-it cease.

It is the blood of Je-sus, The pre-cious, pre-cious blood
These wa-ters are re-fresh-ing, A-bund-ant, rich and free,
Flow on and flow for-ev-er, Flow thro' and thro' my soul,
O stream of life e-ter-nal! Flow in and make me free

By which our souls are ran-somed, And rec-on-ciled to God. Oh!
Im-part-ing health e-ter-nal And im-mor-tal-i-ty. Oh!
With pow-er and with cleansing, Till thou hast made me whole. Oh!
From all that can de-file me, From all im-pur-i-ty. Oh!

CHORUS.

Cal-va-ry's stream is flow-ing, Cal-va-ry's stream is flow-ing,

Calvary's Stream is Flowing.

Flow-ing so free for you and me, Cal-va-ry's stream is flow-ing.

173   I will Go to Jesus Now.

EDWARD JONES.

BENJ. A. STUBBINS.

1. { Come, hum-ble sin - ner, in whose breast A thousand tho'ts re-volve,
   { Come with your guilt and fear oppressed, And [*Omit.* . . . .]

2. { I'll go to Je - sus, tho' my sin Like mountains round me close;
   { I know his courts, I'll en - ter in, What - [*Omit.* . . . .]

CHORUS.

make this last re - solve: I will go,   I will go,

ev - er may op - pose.   I will go to Jesus now, I will go to Jesus now,

Yes, I will go to Je - sus now,   To be saved,

to Jesus now,   I will go,

To be saved,   Be - fore his cross I'll hum-bly bow.

I will go,

3 Prostrate I'll lie before his throne,
   And there my guilt confess;
I'll tell him, I'm a wretch undone
   Without his sovereign grace.

4 I cannot perish if I go—
   I'll call "while he is nigh;"
For if I stay away, I know
   I must forever die.

174 'Tis Blessed to Trust.

G. Tabor Thompson. Alt

A. Barringer.

1. Trusting each day...... in the words of the Sav-ior, Shap-ing my
2. Working each day...... for the cause of the Sav-ior, Gath-er-ing
3. Sing-ing each day.. .... to his praise and his glo-ry, Sing-ing of

1. Trust-ing, I'm trusting each day in the words of the Sav-ior,
2. Work-ing, I'm working each day for the cause of the Sav-ior,
3. Sing-ing, I'm sing-ing each day to his praise and his glo-ry,

life........ by his gentle commands, Sweet are the prom - - is-es
jew - - - els for Je-sus, my King, Cheering the weak.... and the
Christ..... and his wonderful love, Telling in song ...... un-to

Shap-ing my life by his gen-tle commands; And oh, how sweet are the promi-ses
Gath-er-ing jew-els for Je-sus, my King; Cheering, I'm cheering the weak and the
Sing-ing of Christ and his wonderful love; Telling, I'm telling in song un-to

all in my fa-vor, So I am trust - - ing my all in his hands.
faint-hearted ev - er, Glad that some souls..... to the Lord I may bring.
oth-ers the sto - ry, Hop-ing to lead...... them to mansions a-bove.

all in my fa-vor, So I am trusting my all in his hands.
faint-hearted ev - er, Glad that some souls to the Lord I may bring.
oth-ers the sto - ry, Hop-ing to lead them to mansions a-bove.

Chorus.

'Tis bless-ed to trust.............. in the words of my
'Tis bless-ed to trust in the words of my

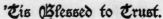

'Tis Blessed to Trust.

Sav - - - - ior, To trust ev'ry day............. and to trust ev'ry
words of my Savior and King, To trust ev-'ry day as you go on life's

night;............. To work to win souls.......... to his
way, and to trust ev-'ry night; To work to win souls, and the

love and his fa - - - - - - - - vor; And rest then at
lost to his love and his fa- vor to bring, And rest then at

light...............
home.............. ior...... in the mansions of light, in the mansions of light.
home in the beautiful mansions of love and of light, in the mansions of light.
light...............

175

The Precious Blood.
Key of E.

1 The cross! the cross! the blood-stained
   The hallow'd cross I see! [cross!
   Reminding me of precious blood
   That once was shed for me.

CHO.–O the blood! the precious blood!
   That Jesus shed for me
   Upon the cross in crimson flood,
   Just now by faith I see.

2 A thousand, thousand fountains spring
   Up from the throne of God;
   But none to me such blessings bring
   As Jesus' precious blood.

3 By faith that blood now sweeps away
   My sins, as like a flood;
   Nor lets one guilty blemish stay;
   All praise to Jesus' blood!

    J. H. STOCKTON & WM. McDONALD.

176 Who can it be?

W. A. O.

W. A. OGDEN.

Rather slow. Effective as a solo.

1. I wandered in sor-row and sin, My heart it was heav-y and sore, I heard a voice say-ing, "A-rise, and come in, Oh! wan-der in sor-row no more." Who can it be? Who can it be?
2. I struggled in doubt and in fear, Not knowing to whom I should go, I heard a voice say-ing, "Son, be of good cheer," So sooth-ing-ly, ten-der and low. Who can it be? Who can it be?
3. I heard it a-gain and a-gain, Wher-ev-er my foot-steps did roam; It melt-ed my heart with its pit-y-ing strain, It light-ed my soul of its gloom. Oh, it was thee! Oh, it was thee!
4. I turned to my Fa-ther a-bove, I read of his prom-is-es sure, I thought of my Sav-ior, his cross and his love, And oh, what a friend I found there! Oh, what a friend! Oh, what a friend!
5. I'm grop-ing in darkness no more, His glo-ry il-lum-ines my way, I'm walk-ing by faith, and his prom-is-es are My sol-ace and joy ev-'ry day. Yes, ev-'ry day! Yes, ev-'ry day!

REFRAIN.

Rit. > > > >   *Ad lib.*

Thus I was wondering, Who can it be Ten-der-ly calling to me?
Thus I was wondering, Who can it be Ten-der-ly calling to me!
Sav-ior of men, oh, my Jesus,'twas thee Sav-ior thou'st been unto me.
Sav-ior of men thou hast been unto me, Savior thou'st been unto me.
Je-sus of Naz-a-reth lighteth my way, Jesus now lighteth my way.

177 Hear and Answer Prayer.

FANNY J. CROSBY.   WM. J. KIRKPATRICK.

1. I am pray-ing, blessed Sav-ior, To be more and more like thee;
2. I am pray-ing, blessed Sav-ior, For a faith so clear and bright
3. I am pray-ing to be humbled By the power of grace di-vine,
4. I am pray-ing, blessed Sav-ior, And my con-stant prayer shall be

I am pray-ing that thy Spir-it Like a dove may rest on me.
That its eye will see thy glo-ry Thro' the deep-est, dark-est night.
To be clothed up-on with meekness, And to have no will but thine.
For a per-fect con-se-cra-tion, That shall make me more like thee.

CHORUS.

Thou who know-est all my weak-ness, Thou who knowest all my care,

While I plead each precious prom-ise, Hear, oh, hear and answer prayer.

178 'Tis the Dear Lord Calling.

E. A. H.

Rev. Elisha A. Hoffman.

BASS SOLO, or TENOR 8va. using small notes.

1. Hark! what sound salutes your ear? Whose the gen - tle voice you hear,
2. Heard you ev - er tones so sweet, Words that with such pow'r en-treat,
3. Oh! re-spond to Je - sus' call; At his feet, re - pent-ant, fall;

ORGAN.

Whisp'-ring soft - ly, ten - der - ly: "Come, oh! come to me?"
Press - ing on your heart the plea: "Come, oh! come to me?"
Heed his sweet and ear - nest plea: "Come, oh! come to me."

QUARTET.

'Tis the dear Lord call - ing, 'Tis the dear Lord call - ing,
gen - tly call - ing, soft- ly call-ing,

Call - ing, call - ing, "Come, oh! come to me,"
Ev - er call-ing, gen-tly call-ing,

'Tis the Dear Lord Calling.

Soft - ly, mild - ly, sweet - ly call - ing, "Come, oh! come to me."

179

In That Day.

J. McPHAIL.

JOHN McPHAIL.

1. All those who love and o - bey my word, In that day,
2. They shall be mine, saith the Lord of hosts, In that day,
3. They shall be with me for - ev - er - more, In that day,

In that day, They shall re - ceive a great re - ward In that day.
In that day, When I shall make my jew - els up, In that day.
In that day, And all their tri - als will be o'er In that day.

CHORUS.

They to my pre - cepts are al - ways true, Do - ing my will in the

work they do; I shall be with them and crown them too, In that day.

In His Name We Meet.

S. F. SMITH.

FREDERIC W. ROOT.

1. Made one in Christ by ho - liest ties, In his dear love we meet;
2. We hold one Lord, one cen - tral light, Our hopes, our aims are one,
3. Hum-bly in loy - al faith we bow At one Re - deem-er's feet;
4. If blos-soms of the ear - ly spring Are doub-ly sweet and fair,

And all who la - bor in his cause In Christ's dear name we greet.
As plan - ets in their de - vious flight Re - volve a - round one sun.
Our prayers, like clouds of in - cense, rise Be - fore one mer - cy - seat.
Our bud - ding youth to God we bring, And leave the off - ring there.

CHORUS.

One king-dom to our conqu'ring Prince, From sea to sea be giv'n;

His will be done o'er the wide earth Just as 'tis done in heav'n.

181 The World for Christ.

(Tune on opposite page.)

1 Christ, for the world we sing,
The world to Christ we bring,
With love and zeal,
The poor and them that mourn,
The faint and overborne,
Sin sick and sorrow worn,
Whom Christ doth heal.

2 Christ for the world we sing,
The world to Christ we bring,
With one accord:
With us the work to share,
With us reproach to dare,
With us the cross to bear,
For Christ our Lord.

SAMUEL WOLCOTT.

182 My Country, 'tis of Thee.

S. F. SMITH.   Tune, AMERICA.

1. My coun - try, 'tis of thee, Sweet land of lib - er - ty,
2. My na - tive coun - try, thee, Land of the no - ble free,
3. Let mu - sic swell the breeze, And ring from all the trees
4. Our fa - thers' God, to thee, Au - thor of lib - er - ty,

Of thee I sing; Land where my fa - thers died, Land of the
Thy name I love; I love thy rocks and rills, Thy woods and
Sweet free-dom's song; Let mor - tal tongues a - wake, Let all that
To thee we sing; Long may our land be bright, With freedom's

Cres.

pil - grims' pride, From ev - 'ry mount-ain side, Let free-dom ring.
tem - pled hills, My heart with rapt-ure thrills, Like that a - bove.
breathe par - take, Let rocks their si - lence break, The sound pro - long.
ho - ly light, Pro - tect us by thy might, Great God, our King.

---

183 We'll Endeavor. (Tune above.)

1 "Christian Endeavor" bright,
Offspring of truth and light,
  Sent from above.
We'll stoutly strive to stand,
For this most glorious band—
Strong pillars of our land—
  Our faith and love.

2 Our banner onward wave,
As guiding star to save,
  Souls for our King.
We'll do our best to fight
For all that's true and right,
Until that day of light
  Victory bring.

3 United Christians we
Would praise and pray to thee,
  Our Savior, Lord.
We'll strive at last to win,
The mansions free from sin.
Trusting, we'll enter in,
  To live with God.

184 Ye Christian Workers.

(Tune, ZION. No. 269.)

1 To the front, ye Christian workers!
In your blessed Master's name,
Stand and nobly, bravely battle;
Win eternal, fadeless fame,
  Looking upward,
Till your hearts are all aflame!

2 To the front, ye Christian workers!
See the dying everywhere;
Cursed by sin, and bruised by Satan,
How they need your help and care!
  Lifting upward,
In their rescue have a share.

3 To the front, ye Christian workers!
God has much for you to do;
Hear his calls, and do his bidding,
Prove yourselves his servants true;
  Look up, lift up,
Till the crown is given you!

REV. T. C. NEAL.

Over the Rolling Sea.

E. A. HOFFMAN.

R. B. MAHAFFEY.

1. O-ver the roll-ing sea, Ma-ny the voic-es ap-peal-ing to me;
2. O-ver the roll-ing sea, Mill-ions are per-ish-ing, Lord, without thee;
3. O-ver the roll-ing sea, There is a mis-sion of mer-cy for me;

Grop-ing in the dark-ness they, And to us for light they pray;
We are bless'd with Gos-pel light, While they grope in hea-then night,
Souls by years of sin de-praved By my ef-forts may be saved,

ff *pp*

O, their cry rings pit-eous-ly O'er the waves of the deep, roll-ing sea,
And we send not, O the shame! Help to them in the Sav-ior's dear name,
If I help to send the light To the peo-ple now shadowed in night

pp Rit.

O-ver the roll-ing sea, O-ver the roll-ing sea!
O-ver the roll-ing sea, O-ver the roll-ing sea!
O-ver the roll-ing sea, O-ver the roll-ing sea!

CHORUS.

O - ver the sea,.......... Call - ing to me,..........
O - ver the sea, Call-ing to me,

Over the Rolling Sea.

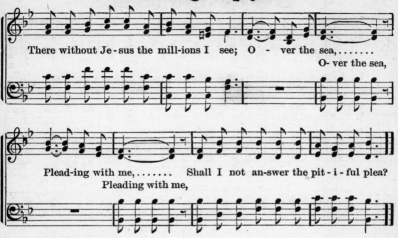

There without Je-sus the mill-ions I see; O - ver the sea,.......
O- ver the sea,

Plead-ing with me,....... Shall I not an-swer the pit - i - ful plea?
Pleading with me,

186 The Lord's Prayer.

Reverently.

1. Our Father which art in heaven, hallowed | be thy | name, ‖ Thy kingdom come, thy will be done in | earth, as it | is in | heaven.

2. Give us this day our | daily | bread, ‖ And forgive us our trespasses, as we for-give | them that | trespass a- | gainst us.

3. And lead us not into temptation, but deliver | us from | evil; ‖ For thine is the kingdom, and the power and the | glory for- | ever and | ever. ‖ A- | men.

187 Gloria Patri.

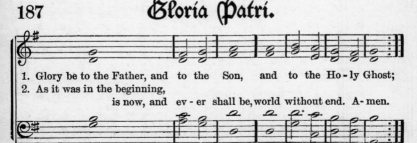

1. Glory be to the Father, and to the Son, and to the Ho - ly Ghost;
2. As it was in the beginning,
is now, and ev - er shall be, world without end. A- men.

188 The Blood is All My Plea.

Rev. F. C. Baker.

E. F. Miller.

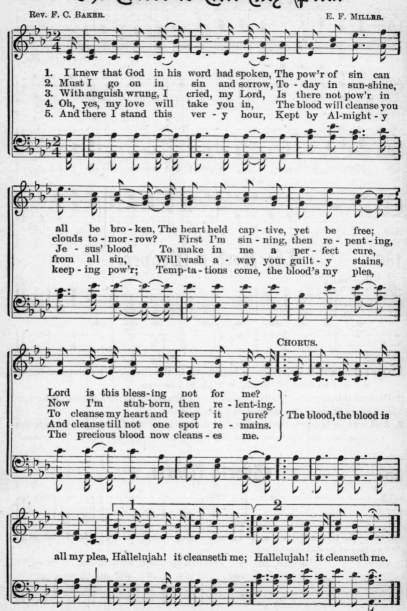

1. I knew that God in his word had spoken, The pow'r of sin can
2. Must I go on in sin and sorrow, To-day in sun-shine,
3. With anguish wrung, I cried, my Lord, Is there not pow'r in
4. Oh, yes, my love will take you in, The blood will cleanse you
5. And there I stand this ver-y hour, Kept by Al-might-y

all be bro-ken, The heart held cap-tive, yet be free;
clouds to-mor-row? First I'm sin-ning, then re-pent-ing,
Je-sus' blood To make in me a per-fect cure,
from all sin, Will wash a-way your guilt-y stains,
keep-ing pow'r; Temp-ta-tions come, the blood's my plea,

CHORUS.

Lord is this bless-ing not for me?
Now I'm stub-born, then re-lent-ing,
To cleanse my heart and keep it pure?
And cleanse till not one spot re-mains.
The precious blood now cleans-es me.

⎫
⎬ The blood, the blood is
⎭

1.

2.

all my plea, Hallelujah! it cleanseth me; Hallelujah! it cleanseth me.

189 Unto You is Everlasting Life.

W. A. O.

W. A. OGDEN.

1. Hear the prom-ise of the Lord, As re-cord-ed in his word,
2. Wea-ry pil-grim on the road To the judgment seat of God,
3. Cast on Je-sus all your care, And your bur-den he will bear,

"Un-to you is ev-er-last-ing life!" Heav-y-la-den and distress'd,
"Un-to you is ev-er-last-ing life!" If on Je-sus you be-lieve,
"Un-to you is ev-er-last-ing life!" In the strait and nar-row way,

Come, and I will give you rest, "Un-to you is ev-er-last-ing life!"
And his bless-ed word re-ceive, "Un-to you is ev-er-last-ing life!"
He will lead you day by day! "Un-to you is ev-er-last-ing life!"

CHORUS.

"Everlasting life" the promise reads, While at God's right hand the Savior pleads;

Will you come to-day, making Christ your stay? For with him is everlasting life.

190 Follow all the Way.

Rev. ELISHA A. HOFFMAN.　　　　Arr. by IRA ORWIG HOFFMAN.

TRIO.

1. I can hear my Sav-ior call-ing, In the tend'rest ac-cents call-ing;
2. Tho' the way be dark and dreary, Tho' my feet be worn and wea-ry,
3. Je-sus, ev-er go be-fore me, Shin-ing heaven's sunlight o'er me,
4. Thro' the val-ley safe-ly lead me, Heav'nly man-na dai-ly feed me;
5. In thy heart's af-fec-tion hold me, In thy arms of love en-fold me,

On my ear these words are falling, "Take thy cross, and dai-ly fol-low me."
Yet my heart keeps bright and cheery As I fol-low, fol-low all the way.
And when weak, by grace re-store me As I fol-low, fol-low all the way.
Ev-'ry hour, dear Lord, I need thee As I fol-low, fol-low all the way.
And with thine own grace uphold me, As I fol-low, fol-low all the way.

CHORUS.

I will take my cross and fol-low, My dear Sav-ior I will fol-low,

Where he leads me I will fol-low, I'll go with him, with him all the way.

6 I will never leave thee, never;
　Faithful I will be forever;
　Help me in my weak endeavor
　　Thee to follow, follow all the way.

7 Thro' death's dark and gloomy portal,
　Leaving there this body mortal,
　Into yonder home immortal
　I will follow, follow all the way.

There is Joy.

Margaret Moody.

W. A. Ogden.

1. When a sin-ner comes, as a sin-ner may, There is joy,.......... there is joy;........ When he turns to God in the gos-pel way,
2. When a soul is born in the king-dom bright, There is joy,.......... there is joy;........ When it walks by faith in the gos-pel light,
3. When a pil-grim comes to the riv-er wide, There is joy,.......... there is joy;........ When he dwells se-cure on the oth-er side,

There is joy, there is joy,

There is joy,........ there is joy. There is joy a-mong the

There is joy,

an-gels, And their harps with mu-sic ring,....... When a

mu-sic ring,

sin-ner comes re-pent-ing, Bend-ing low be-fore the King.

CHORUS.

192 Believe on the Crucified One.

C. H. G.

CHAS. H. GABRIEL.

1. Oh! why will you turn from the Savior away? He's calling you tender - ly,
2. He pleads by the anguish he suffer'd for thee, By nail-prints that bound him to
3. Why wander a-way in the darkness a-far? You've only to knock, for the

call-ing to-day; There's on-ly one refuge from death and the grave, That
Cal-va-ry's tree; By vic-to-ry o-ver the grave and its gloom, Oh,
door is a - jar; Come quickly and give him your heart while you may, Oh,

CHORUS.

ref - uge is Je - sus, the might-y to save. Believe on the cru-ci-fied
sin - ner, be-lieve him, he's calling you,—come!
haste to re-ceive him, he's wait-ing to - day.   The

One,...... Be-lieve on the cru - ci - fied One;...... No
cru-ci-fied One,   the cru-ci-fied One;

longer delay, he is calling today, He waits to receive you, come home, come home.

193. I Am the Lord's Forever.

E. A. H.
Rev. Elisha A. Hoffman.

1. My gladsome heart these words repeat; "I am the Lord's for-ev - er!"
2. Too long and far from Christ I strayed, But he for-sook me nev - er;
3. 'Twas Christ, the Lamb of Cal- va - ry, That loved and sought me ev - er,

And ev-'ry time they seem more sweet! Oh, praise his name for-ev - er!
Now walk-ing in the nar - row way, I am the Lord's for-ev - er!
That broke my chains and set me free; Oh, praise his name for-ev - er!

CHORUS.

Hal - le - lu - jah! hal - le - lu - jah! Light breaks in up - on my soul;

Hal - le - lu - jah! hal - le - lu - jah! Je - sus' blood has made me whole.

4 I am the Lord's! Oh, blessed thought!
  And he will leave me never;
  By Jesus' blood my soul was bought,
  And I am his forever!

5 This is the burden of my song;
  "I am the Lord's forever!"
  And naught that earth can offer me
  My heart from Christ can sever.

194 Seeking the Lost.

W. A. O.

W. A. Ogden.

1. Seeking the lost, yes, kindly entreating Wanderers on the mountains astray, "Come unto me," his message repeating, Words of the Master speaking today.

2. Seeking the lost, and pointing to Jesus Souls that are weak and hearts that are sore, Leading them forth in ways of salvation, Showing the path to life evermore.

3. Thus would I go, for Jesus hath call'd me, Him would I follow day unto day; Care for the dying, raise up the fallen, Pointing the lost to Jesus the way.

CHORUS, with Bass Solo obligato.

Going afar, afar upon the mountain, Bringing the wand'rers, the wand'rers back again, Into the fold, the fold of my Redeemer,

Going afar upon the mountain, Bringing the wan — d'rers back again, Into the fold of my Re-deem-er,

BY PERMISSION OF W. A. OGDEN.

182

Seeking the Lost.

Je - sus the Lamb, the Lamb for sin-ners slain

Je - sus the Lamb............. for sin-ners slain.........

195

Pass the Word along.

G. W. D.

GRACE WEISER DAVIS.

1. Je - sus came to save from sin, Pass the word a-long; He can make us
2. To the Sav-ior all may come, Pass the word a-long; All the wan-der -
3. Without money you can buy, Pass the word a-long; Wine and milk that
4. All the lame, and halt, and blind, Pass the word a-long; Here may full sal-
5. All his ben - e - fits embrace, Pass the word a-long; Free - ly now be

CHORUS.

pure within, Pass the word a-long. Good news! good news!
ers from home, Pass the word a-long.
sat - is - fy, Pass the word a-long.
va - tion find, Pass the word a-long.
saved by grace, Pass the word a-long. Good news! good news!

Pass the word along; Good news! good news! Pass the word a-long.
Good news! good news!

196   O Day of Rest and Gladness.

C. WORDSWORTH.   Tune, MENDEBRAS. 7, 5.

1. { O day of rest and glad-ness, O day of joy and light,
   O balm of care and sad-ness, Most beau-ti-ful, most bright:

On thee, the high and low-ly, Through a-ges joined in tune,

Sing "Ho-ly, ho-ly, ho-ly," To the great God Tri-une.

2 To-day on weary nations
  The heavenly manna falls;
To holy convocations
  The silver trumpet calls,
Where gospel light is glowing
  With pure and radiant beams,
And living water flowing
  With soul-refreshing streams.

3 New graces ever gaining
  From this our day of rest,
We reach the rest remaining
  To spirits of the blest;
To Holy Ghost be praises,
  To Father, and to Son;
The Church her voice upraises
  To thee, blest Three in One.

197   A Closer Walk with God.

Tune, BALERMA. C. M.

1 Oh, for a closer walk with God,
  A calm and heavenly frame;
A light to shine upon the road
  That leads me to the Lamb.

2 The dearest idol I have known,
  Whate'er that idol be,
Help me to tear it from thy throne,
  And worship only thee.

3 Return, O holy Dove, return,
  Sweet messenger of rest!
I hate the sins that made thee mourn,
  And drove thee from my breast.

4 So shall my walk be close with God,
  Calm and serene my frame;
So purer light shall mark the road
  That leads me to the Lamb.

WM. COWPER.

CHARLES WESLEY.   Tune, LOVE DIVINE. 8, 7. D.

1. Love di-vine, all love ex-cel-ling, Joy of heav'n to earth come down!

Fix in us thy hum-ble dwelling; All thy faith-ful mer-cies crown.

D.S.—Vis-it us with thy sal-va-tion; En-ter ev-'ry trembling heart.

Je-sus, thou art all com-pas-sion, Pure, un-bound-ed love thou art;

2 Breathe, O breathe thy loving Spirit
   Into every troubled breast!
Let us all in thee inherit,
   Let us find that second rest.
Take away our bent to sinning;
   Alpha and Omega be;
End of faith, as its beginning,
   Set our hearts at liberty.

3 Finish then thy new creation;
   Pure and spotless let us be;
Let us see thy great salvation,
   Perfectly restored in thee:
Changed from glory into glory,
   Till in heaven we take our place,
Till we cast our crowns before thee,
   Lost in wonder, love, and praise.

---

199   Evils of Intemperance.
        (Tune, Boylston. No. 232.)

1 Mourn for the thousands slain,
   The youthful and the strong;
Mourn for the wine-cup's fearful reign,
   And the deluded throng.

2 Mourn for the lost,—but call,
   Call to the strong, the free;
Rouse them to shun that dreadful fall,
   And to the refuge flee.

3 Mourn for the lost,—but pray,
   Pray to our God above,
To break the fell destroyer's sway,
   And show his saving love.

200   What Ruin!
        (Tune, Azmon. No. 210.)

1 What ruin hath intemperance wro't!
   How widely roll its waves!
How many myriads hath it brought
   To fill dishonored graves!

2 Stretch forth thy hand, O God, our
   And break the galling chain; [King,
Deliverance to the captive bring,
   And end the usurper's reign.

3 The cause of temperance is thine own;
   Our plans and efforts bless;
We trust, O Lord, in thee alone
   To crown them with success.

201

JOHN H. NEWMAN.

Lead, Kindly Light.

JOHN B. DYKES.

1. Lead, kindly Light, amid th'encircling gloom, Lead thou me on; The night is
2. I was not ev - er thus, nor prayed that thou Shouldst lead me on; I loved to
3. So long thy pow'r hath blest me, sure it still Will lead me on O'er moor and

dark, and I am far from home, Lead thou me on. Keep thou my feet; I
choose and see my path; but now Lead thou me on. I loved the gar - ish
fen, o'er crag and torrent, till The night is gone. And with the morn those

do not ask to see The dis-tant scene; one step enough for me.
day; and, spite of fears, Pride ruled my will; remember not past years.
an-gel fac - es smile, Which I have loved long since, and lost awhile.

202

ISAAC WATTS.

Am I A Soldier?

Tune:
ARLINGTON. C. M.

203

Awake, My Soul.

1 Am I a soldier of the cross,—
   A follower of the Lamb,—
And shall I fear to own his cause,
   Or blush to speak his name?

2 Are there no foes for me to face?
   Must I not stem the flood?
Is this vile world a friend to grace,
   To help me on to God?

3 Sure I must fight if I would reign;
   Increase my courage, Lord!
I'll bear the toil, endure the pain,
   Supported by thy word.

1 Awake, my soul, stretch every nerve,
   And press with vigor on;
A heavenly race demands thy zeal,
   And an immortal crown.

2 A cloud of witnesses around
   Hold thee in full survey;
Forget the steps already trod,
   And onward urge thy way.

3 Blest Savior, introduced by thee,
   Have I my race begun;
And, crowned with victory, at thy feet
   I'll lay my honors down.

PHILIP DODDRIDGE.

Jesus Shall Reign.

ISAAC WATTS.   Tune, MIGDOL. L. M.

1. Je-sus shall reign where'er the sun Does his suc - ces - sive journeys run;
2. From north to south the princes meet, To pay their homage at his feet;

His kingdom spread from shore to shore, Till moons shall wax and wane no more.
While western empires own their Lord, And savage tribes at-tend his word.

3 To him shall endless prayer be made,
And endless praises crown his head;
His name like sweet perfume shall rise
With every morning sacrifice.

4 People and realms of every tongue
Dwell on his love with sweetest song,
And infant voices shall proclaim
Their early blessings on his name.

205 O Thou in Whose Presence.

JOSEPH SWAIN.   Tune, MEDITATION. 11, 8.

1. O thou in whose presence my soul takes delight, On whom in affliction I call,
2. Where dost thou, dear shepherd, resort with thy sheep, To feed them in pastures of love?

My comfort by day and my song in the night, My hope, my salvation, my all!
Say, why in the valley of death should I weep, Or alone in this wilderness rove?

3 He looks! and ten thousands of angels
rejoice,
And myriads wait for his word;
He speaks! and eternity, filled with his
Re-echoes the praise of the Lord. [voice,

4 Dear Shepherd, I hear, and will follow
thy call;
I know the sweet sound of thy voice;
Restore and defend me, for thou art my all
And in thee I will ever rejoice.

206 Rescue the Perishing.

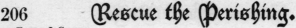

FANNY J. CROSBY.　　　　　　　　　　　　　　　　　　W. H. DOANE.

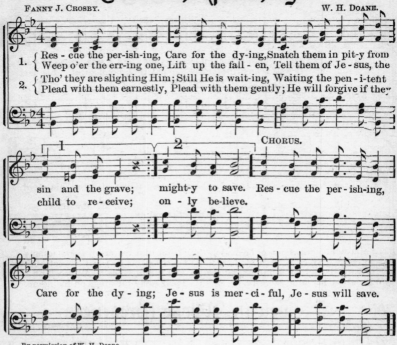

1. { Res - cue the per-ish-ing, Care for the dy-ing, Snatch them in pit-y from
   { Weep o'er the err-ing one, Lift up the fall - en, Tell them of Je - sus, the

2. { Tho' they are slighting Him; Still He is wait-ing, Waiting the pen - i-tent
   { Plead with them earnestly, Plead with them gently; He will forgive if they

1 sin and the grave; *2* might-y to save.

child to re-ceive; on - ly be-lieve.

CHORUS.

Res - cue the per-ish-ing, Care for the dy - ing; Je - sus is mer - ci - ful, Je - sus will save.

By permission of W. H. Doane.

3 Down in the human heart,
　Crushed by the tempter,　[store;
Feelings lie buried that grace can re-
　Touched by a loving heart,
　Wakened by kindness, [once more.
Chords that were broken will vibrate

4 Rescue the perishing,
　Duty demands it;　[provide:
Strength for thy labor the Lord will
　Back to the narrow way
　Patiently win them;
Tell the poor wanderer a Savior has died.

207　Shall We Gather at the River?
Key of E♭.

1 Shall we gather at the river
　Where bright angel feet have trod?
　With its crystal tide forever
　Flowing by the throne of God.

CHO.—Yes, we'll gather at the river,
　The beautiful, the beautiful river—
　Gather with the saints at the river,
　That flows by the throne of God.

2 On the margin of the river,
　Washing up its silver spray,

We will walk and worship ever,
　All the happy golden day.

3 Ere we reach the shining river,
　Lay we every burden down;
Grace our spirits will deliver,
　And provide a robe and crown.

4 At the smiling of the river,
　Mirror of the Savior's face,
Saints whom death will never sever,
　Lift their songs of saving grace.

5 Soon we'll reach the silver river,
　Soon our pilgrimage will cease;
Soon our happy hearts will quiver,
　With the melody of peace.

Rev. ROBERT LOWRY.

By permission.

208　Sing We to our God.
(Tune, PLEYEL'S HYMN. No. 221.)

Sing we to our God above,
Praise eternal as his love;
Praise him, all ye heavenly host,
Father, Son and Holy Ghost.

CHARLES WESLEY.

209 Forever Here my Rest.

CHARLES WESLEY.

Tune, AVON. C. M.

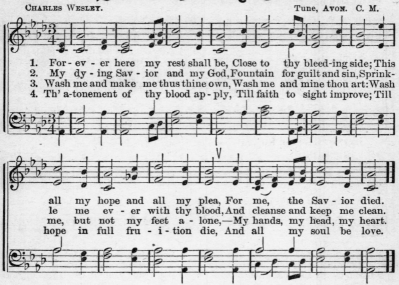

1. For - ev - er here my rest shall be, Close to thy bleed-ing side; This
2. My dy - ing Sav - ior and my God, Fountain for guilt and sin, Sprink-
3. Wash me and make me thus thine own, Wash me and mine thou art: Wash
4. Th' a-tonement of thy blood ap - ply, Till faith to sight improve; Till

all my hope and all my plea, For me, the Sav - ior died.
le me ev - er with thy blood, And cleanse and keep me clean.
me, but not my feet a - lone,—My hands, my head, my heart.
hope in full fru - i - tion die, And all my soul be love.

210 A Heart to Praise my God.

CHARLES WESLEY.

Tune, AZMON. C. M.

1 O, for a heart to praise my God,
A heart from sin set free!
A heart that always feels thy blood
So freely spilt for me!

2 A heart resigned, submissive, meek,
My great Redeemer's throne;
Where only Christ is heard to speak,
Where Jesus reigns alone.

3 A heart in every thought renewed,
And full of love divine;
Perfect, and right, and pure, and good,
A copy, Lord, of thine.

4 Thy nature, gracious Lord, impart;
Come quickly from above;
Write thy new name upon my heart,
Thy new, best name of Love.

211 The Joyful Sound.

1 Salvation! Oh, the joyful sound!
What pleasure to our ears;
A sovereign balm for every wound,
A cordial for our fears.

2 Salvation! let the echo fly
The spacious earth around,
While all the armies of the sky
Conspire to raise the sound.

3 Salvation! O thou bleeding Lamb!
To thee the praise belongs;
Salvation shall inspire our hearts,
And dwell upon our tongues.

ISAAC WATTS.

212 The Great Physician.

WILLIAM HUNTER.

Arr. by Rev. J. H. STOCKTON.

FINE.

1. { The great Phy - si - cian now is near, The sym - pa - thiz - ing Je - sus,
   He speaks the drooping heart to cheer, Oh! hear the voice of Je - sus.

2. { Your ma - ny sins are all for-giv'n, Oh! hear the voice of Je - sus,
   Go on your way in peace to heav'n, And wear a crown with Je - sus.

D.C. Sweet-est car - ol ev - er sung, Je - sus, bless-ed Je - sus.

REFRAIN.

D. C.

Sweetest note in ser - aph song, Sweetest name on mor-tal tongue,

3 His name dispels my guilt and fear,
   No other name but Jesus:
   Oh! how my soul delights to hear
   The charming name of Jesus.

4 And when to that bright world above
   We rise to see our Jesus,
   We'll sing around the throne of love,
   The name, the name of Jesus.

BY PER. OF J. J. HOOD, OWNER OF COPYRIGHT.

213 Holy Spirit, Faithful Guide.

M. M. W.

M. M. WELLS.

FINE.

1. { Ho - ly Spir - it, faith-ful guide, Ev - er near the Christian's side;
   Gen - tly lead us by the hand, Pil-grims in a des - ert land;

2. { Ev - er pres-ent, tru - est friend, Ev - er near thine aid to lend,
   Leave us not to doubt and fear, Grop-ing on in dark-ness drear.

3. { When our days of toil shall cease, Wait-ing still for sweet re - lease,
   Noth-ing left but heav'n and pray'r, Wond'ring if our names are there;

D.C.—Whisp'ring soft-ly, "wand'rer come, Fol - low me, I'll guide thee home."

D. C.

Wea - ry souls for - e'er re - joice, While they hear that sweet - est voice,
When the storms are rag - ing sore, Hearts grow faint, and hopes give o'er,
Wad - ing deep the dis - mal flood, Plead-ing naught but Je - sus' blood;

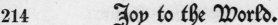

Joy to the World.

214

ISAAC WATTS.

Tune, ANTIOCH.   C. M.

1 Joy to the world! the Lord is come;
Let earth receive her King;
Let every heart prepare him room,
And heaven and nature sing.

2 Joy to the world! the Savior reigns;
Let men their songs employ;
While fields and floods, rocks, hills and
Repeat the sounding joy.   [plains,

3 He rules the world with truth and
grace,
And makes the nations prove
The glories of his righteousness,
And wonders of his love.

215   O for a Thousand Tongues.
Tune below.

1 O for a thousand tongues, to sing
My great Redeemer's praise!
The glories of my God and King,
The triumphs of his grace!

2 Jesus! the name that charms our fears,
That bids our sorrows cease;
'Tis music in the sinner's ears,
'Tis life, and health, and peace.

3 He breaks the power of canceled sin,
He sets the prisoner free;
His blood can make the foulest clean;
His blood availed for me.

216   ## All Hail the Power.

E. PERRONET.

Tune, CORONATION.   C. M.

1. All hail the pow'r of Je-sus' name! Let an-gels prostrate fall,
2. Let ev-'ry kin-dred, ev-'ry tribe, On this ter-res-trial ball,
3. Oh, that with yon-der sa-cred throng We at his feet may fall;

Bring forth the roy-al di-a-dem, And crown him Lord of all;
To him all maj-es-ty ascribe, And crown him Lord of all;
We'll join the ev-er-lasting song, And crown him Lord of all;

Bring forth the roy-al di-a-dem, And crown him Lord of all.
To him all maj-es-ty as-cribe, And crown him Lord of all.
We'll join the ev-er-lasting song, And crown him Lord of all.

217

Come, Sinner, Come.

W. E. WITTER.   H. R. PALMER.

1. While Je-sus whispers to you, Come, sin-ner, come! While we are
2. Are you too heav-y-lad-en? Come, sin-ner, come! Je-sus will
3. Oh, hear his ten-der pleading, Come, sin-ner, come! Come and re-

pray-ing for you, Come, sin-ner, come! Now is the time to own him,
bear your burden, Come, sin-ner, come! Je-sus will not de-ceive you,
ceive the blessing, Come, sin-ner, come! While Je-sus whis-pers to you,

Come, sin-ner, come! Now is the time to know him, Come, sin-ner, come!
Come, sin-ner, come! Je-sus can now redeem you, Come, sin-ner, come!
Come, sin-ner, come! While we are praying for you, Come, sin-ner, come!

BY PER. OF H. R. PALMER OWNER OF COPYRIGHT.

218 Depth of Mercy.
Tune: PLEYEL'S HYMN, opposite page.

1 Depth of mercy! can there be
Mercy still reserved for me?
Can my God his wrath forbear,—
Me, the chief of sinners, spare?

2 I have long withstood his grace;
Long provoked him to his face;
Would not hearken to his calls,
Grieved him by a thousand falls.

3 Now incline me to repent;
Let me now my sins lament;
Now my foul revolt deplore,
Weep, believe, and sin no more.

4 There for me the Savior stands,
Shows his wounds and spreads his
God is love! I know, I feel; [hands;
Jesus weeps, and loves me still.

CHARLES WESLEY.

219 Holy Bible, Book Divine.
Tune: PLEYEL'S HYMN, opposite page.

1 Holy Bible, book divine,
Precious treasure, thou art mine;
Mine, to tell me whence I came;
Mine to teach me what I am.

2 Mine, to chide me when I rove;
Mine, to show a Savior's love;
Mine art thou to guide my feet;
Mine to judge, condemn, acquit.

3 Mine to comfort in distress,
If the Holy Spirit bless;
Mine, to show by living faith
Man can triumph over death.

4 Mine to tell of joys to come,
And the rebel sinner's doom;
Oh, thou holy book divine,
Precious treasure, thou art mine.

JOHN BURTON, SR.

Jesus now is Calling.

R. E. H.   R. E. HUDSON.

1. Come, ye weary and oppressed, Jesus now is calling you; Come to him, he'll
2. Tho' your sins like mountains rise, Jesus now is calling you;   He has made the
3. Tho' your sins like scarlet be,   Jesus now is calling you; From your sins he'll
4. Come, ye wand'rers from the fold, Jesus now is calling you;   Oh! his love can

REFRAIN.

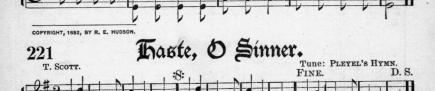

give you rest—Still he bids you come.
sac-ri-fice—Still he bids you come.
set you free—Still he bids you come.
ne'er be told—Still he bids you come.   Jesus now is calling,   Calling,
                                                    calling,   calling,

calling;   Je - sus now is   call-ing you—Call-ing you   to come.
   call-ing;

COPYRIGHT, 1882, BY R. E. HUDSON.

221

Haste, O Sinner.

T. SCOTT.   Tune: PLEYEL'S HYMN.
                                             FINE.   D. S.

1 Haste, O sinner, now be wise;
   Stay not for the morrow's sun;
Wisdom if you still despise
   Harder is it to be won.

2 Haste, and mercy now implore;
   Stay not for the morrow's sun,
Lest thy season should be o'er
   E'er this evening's stage be run.

3 Haste, O sinner, now return,
   Stay not for the morrow's sun,
Lest thy lamp should cease to burn
   Ere salvation's work is done.

222   **Why Will Ye Die.**

1 Sinners, turn, why will ye die?
   God, your Maker, asks you why;
   God, who did your being give,
   Made you with himself to live.

2 Sinners, turn, why will ye die?
   God, your Savior, asks you why;
   Will ye not in him believe?
   He has died that ye might live.

3 Sinners, turn, why will ye die?
   God, the Spirit, asks you why;
   Often with you has he strove,
   Wooed you to embrace his love.

There is a Fountain.

WM. COWPER.　　　　　　　　　　WESTERN MELODY. C. M.

1. { There is a fount-ain filled with blood, Drawn from Im-man-uel's veins;
And sin-ners plung'd beneath that flood, [*Omit.*

D. C. And sin-ners plung'd beneath that flood, [*Omit.*

FINE.　　　　　　　　　　　　　　　D. C.

Lose all their guilty stains, Lose all their guilty stains, Lose all their guilty stains,

Lose all their guilty stains.

2 The dying thief rejoiced to see
　That fountain in his day;
And there may I, though vile as he,
　Wash all my sins away.

3 Ere since, by faith, I saw the stream
　Thy flowing wounds supply,

Redeeming love has been my theme,
　And shall be, till I die.

4 Then in a nobler, sweeter song,
　I'll sing thy power to save,
When this poor, lisping, stamm'ring
　Lies silent in the grave. 　[tongue

224 I Stretch my Hands to Thee.

CHARLES WESLEY.　　　　　　Tune: I DO BELIEVE. C. M.

1. Fa - ther, I stretch my hands to thee, No oth - er help I know;
2. What did thine on - ly Son en - dure, Be - fore I drew my breath;
Cho.—I do be - lieve, I now be - lieve, That Je - sus died for me,

If thou with-draw thy-self from me, Ah, whither shall I go?
What pain, what la - bor to se - cure My soul from end - less death!
And thro' his blood, his pre-cious blood, I shall from sin be free.

3 O Jesus, could I this believe,
　I now should feel thy power;
And all my wants thou wouldst re-
　In this accepted hour. 　[lieve,

4 Author of faith, to thee I lift
　My weary, longing eyes;
O let me now receive that gift!
　My soul without it dies.

225 — Blest Be the Tie.

Rev. John Fawcett.

Tune, Dennis. S. M.

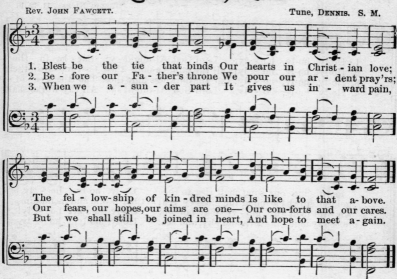

1. Blest be the tie that binds Our hearts in Christ-ian love;
2. Be - fore our Fa - ther's throne We pour our ar - dent pray'rs;
3. When we a - sun - der part It gives us in - ward pain,

The fel - low-ship of kin - dred minds Is like to that a - bove.
Our fears, our hopes, our aims are one— Our com-forts and our cares.
But we shall still be joined in heart, And hope to meet a - gain.

226 — O Spirit of the Living God.

James Montgomery.

Tune, Rockingham. L. M.

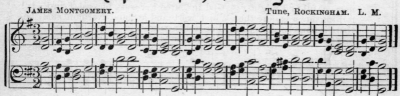

1 O Spirit of the living God,
    In all thy plenitude of grace,
Where'er the foot of man hath trod,
    Descend on our apostate race.

2 Give tongues of fire and hearts of love,
    To preach the reconciling word;
Give power and unction from above,
    Where'er the joyful sound is heard.

3 Be darkness, at thy coming, light;
    Confusion, order in thy path;
Souls without strength, inspire with
        might;
    Bid mercy triumph over wrath.

4 Baptize the nations; far and nigh
    The triumphs of the cross record;
The name of Jesus glorify,
    Till every kindred call him Lord.

227 — Come, Holy Spirit.

1 Come, Holy Spirit, raise our songs
    To reach the wonders of that day,
When, with thy fiery, cloven tongues
    Thou didst such glorious scenes display.

2 Lord, we believe to us and ours,
    The apostolic promise given;
We wait the pentecostal powers,
    The Holy Ghost sent down from heaven.

3 Assembled here with one accord,
    Calmly we wait the promised grace,
The purchase of our dying Lord;
    Come, Holy Ghost, and fill the place.

4 If every one that asks, may find,
    If still thou dost on sinners fall,
Come as a mighty, rushing wind;
    Great grace be now upon us all.

Charles Wesley.

Holy, Holy, Holy.

REGINALD HEBER.

Tune: NICEA. 11, 12, 10.

1. Ho-ly, ho-ly, ho-ly, Lord God Al-might-y! Ear-ly in the morn-ing our song shall rise to thee; Ho-ly, ho-ly, ho-ly, mer-ci-ful and might-y, God in Three Per-sons, blessed Trin-i-ty!

2. Ho-ly, ho-ly, ho-ly! all the saints a-dore thee, Cast-ing down their gold-en crowns a-round the glass-y sea; Cher-u-bim and seraphim fall-ing down be-fore thee, Which wert, and art, and evermore shalt be.

3. Ho-ly, ho-ly, ho-ly! tho' the darkness hide thee, Tho' the eye of sin-ful man thy glo-ry may not see; On-ly thou art ho-ly! there is none be-side thee, Per-fect in power, in love, and pur-i-ty.

4. Ho-ly, ho-ly, ho-ly, Lord God Al-might-y! All thy works shall praise thy name, in earth, and sky, and sea; Ho-ly, ho-ly, ho-ly, mer-ci-ful and might-y, God in Three Per-sons, blessed Trin-i-ty!

---

229 Lord, God, the Holy Ghost.
Tune: BOYLSTON, opposite page.

1 Lord, God, the Holy Ghost!
In this accepted hour,
As on the day of Pentecost,
Descend in all thy power.

2 We meet with one accord
In our appointed place,
And wait the promise of our Lord,—
The Spirit of all grace.

3 Like mighty, rushing wind
Upon the waves beneath,
Move with one impulse every mind;
One soul, one feeling breathe.

4 The young, the old, inspire
With wisdom from above;
And give us hearts and tongues of fire,
To pray, and praise, and love.
J. MONTGOMERY.

230 O Blessed Paraclete.
Tune: BOYLSTON, opposite page.

1 O blessed Paraclete,
Assert thine inward sway;
My body make the temple meet,
For thy perpetual stay.

2 Too long this house of thine
By alien loves possessed,
Has shut from thee its inner shrine,
Kept thee a slighted guest.

3 Now rend, O Spirit blest,
The veil of my poor heart;
Enter thy long forbidden rest,
And nevermore depart.

4 Oh, to be filled with thee!
I ask not aught beside;
For all unholy guests must flee,
If thou in me abide.
A. J. GORDON, by per.

231 Jesus is Mine!

Mrs. C. J. Bonar.   T. E. Perkins.

1. Fade, fade, each earthly joy, Je-sus is mine! Break, ev-'ry
2. Fare-well, ye dreams of night, Je-sus is mine! Lost in this
3. Fare-well, mor-tal-i-ty, Je-sus is mine! Wel-come, e-

ten-der tie, Je-sus is mine! Dark is the wil-der-ness,
dawning light, Je-sus is mine! All that my soul has tried
ter-ni-ty, Je-sus is mine! Wel-come, O loved and blest,

Earth has no resting place, Je-sus a-lone can bless, Je-sus is mine!
Left but a dismal void, Je-sus has sat-is-fied, Je-sus is mine!
Welcome, sweet scenes of rest, Welcome, my Savior's breast, Je-sus is mine!

BY PERMISSION.

232 A Charge to Keep.

Charles Wesley.   Tune: Boylston. S. M.

1 A charge to keep I have;
   A God to glorify:
A never-dying soul to save,
   And fit it for the sky.

2 To serve the present age,
   My calling to fulfil,
O may it all my powers engage
   To do my Master's will.

3 Help me to watch and pray,
   And on thyself rely;
Assured if I my trust betray,
   I shall forever die.

233 Can I yet Delay?

1 And can I yet delay
   My little all to give?
To tear my soul from earth away,
   For Jesus to receive?

2 Nay, but I yield, I yield!
   I can hold out no more:
I sink by dying love compell'd,
   And own the conqueror!

3 Come, and possess me whole,
   Nor hence again remove;
Settle and fix my wavering soul
   With all thy weight of love.

Charles Wesley.

Take Me as I Am.

Rev. J. H. Stockton.

1. Je - sus, my Lord, to thee I cry, Unless thou help me, I must die;
2. Help-less I am, and full of guilt, But yet for me thy blood was spilt,
3. If thou hast work for me to do, Inspire my will, my heart re - new,
4. And when at last the work is done, The bat-tle o'er, the vic - t'ry won,

Oh, bring thy free sal - va - tion nigh, And take me as I am!
And thou canst make me what thou wilt, But take me as I am!
And work both in and by me too, But take me as I am!
Still, still my cry shall be a - lone, Oh, take me as I am!

FINE.

D. S. bring thy free sal - va - tion nigh, And take me as I am!

REFRAIN.

D. S.

Take me as I am, ... Take me as I am, ... Oh,
Take me, take me as I am, Take me, take me as I am;

Just as I Am.

Charlotte Elliott.

Tune: Hamburg.

1 Just as I am without one plea,
But that thy blood was shed for me,
And that thou bid'st me come to thee,
O Lamb of God, I come, I come!

2 Just as I am, and waiting not
To rid my soul of one dark blot, [spot,
To thee whose blood can cleanse each
O Lamb of God, I come, I come!

3 Just as I am, thou wilt receive,
Wilt welcome, pardon, cleanse, relieve,
Because thy promise I believe;
O Lamb of God, I come, I come.

4 Just as I am, thy love unknown,
Has broken every barrier down;
Now to be thine, yea, thine alone,
O Lamb of God, I come!

My Faith Looks Up.

RAY PALMER.

Tune: OLIVET. 6, 4.

3 When ends life's transient dream,
When death's cold, sullen stream
    Shall o'er me roll;
Blest Savior, then, in love
Fear and distress remove
Oh, bear me safe above,
    A ransomed soul!

1 My faith looks up to thee,
Thou Lamb of Calvary;
    Savior divine,
Now hear me while I pray,
Take all my sins away;
Oh, let me from this day,
    Be wholly thine.

2 May thy rich grace impart
Strength to my fainting heart,
    My zeal inspire:
As thou hast died for me,
Oh, may my love to thee
Pure, warm, and changeless be,
    A living fire.

237   Come, Holy Ghost.

1 Come, Holy Ghost, in love,
Shed on us from above
    Thine own bright ray!
Divinely good thou art;
Thy sacred gifts impart
To gladden each sad heart:
    Oh, come to-day!

2 Come, tenderest Friend, and best;
Our most delightful Guest,
    With soothing power:
Rest, which the weary know,
Shade, 'mid the noontide glow,
Peace, when deep griefs o'erflow,
    Cheer us this hour!

ROBERT II, KING OF FRANCE. Tr. by R. PALMER.

238 # Glorying in the Cross.

ISAAC WATTS.

Tune: EUCHARIST. L. M.

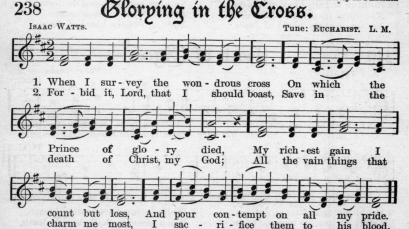

1. When I sur-vey the won-drous cross On which the
2. For-bid it, Lord, that I should boast, Save in the

Prince of glo-ry died, My rich-est gain I
death of Christ, my God; All the vain things that

count but loss, And pour con-tempt on all my pride.
charm me most, I sac-ri-fice them to his blood.

3 See, from his head, his hands, his feet,
Sorrow and love flow mingled down;
Did e'er such love and sorrow meet,
Or thorns compose so rich a crown?

4 Were the whole realm of nature mine,
That were a present far too small:
Love so amazing, so divine,
Demands my soul, my life, my all.

Nothing but the Blood.

R. L.   R. LOWRY.

1. { What can wash a-way my sin? Noth-ing but the blood of Je-sus;
   { What can make me whole a-gain? Noth-ing but the blood of Je-sus.
2. { For my par-don this I see— Noth-ing but the blood of Je-sus;
   { For my cleansing, this my plea,—Noth-ing but the blood of Je-sus.

CHORUS.

Oh, pre-cious is the flow That makes me white as snow;

No oth-er Fount I know, Nothing but the blood of Je-sus.

2 Nothing can for sin atone,
Nothing but the blood of Jesus;
Naught of good that I have done,
Nothing but the blood of Jesus,

4 This is all my hope and peace—
Nothing but the blood of Jesus;
This is all my righteousness—
Nothing but the blood of Jesus.

240

Rock of Ages.

A. TOPLADY.   Tune: TOPLADY. 7.
                                                        FINE.

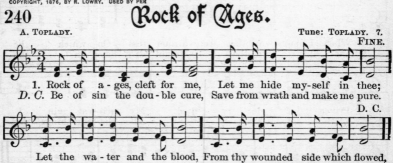

1. Rock of a-ges, cleft for me, Let me hide my-self in thee;
D. C. Be of sin the dou-ble cure, Save from wrath and make me pure.

D. C.

Let the wa-ter and the blood, From thy wounded side which flowed,

2 Could my tears forever flow,
Could my zeal no languor know,
These for sin could not atone;
Thou must save, and thou alone:
In my hand no price I bring;
Simply to thy cross I cling.

3 While I draw this fleeting breath,
When my eyes shall close in death,
When I rise to worlds unknown,
And behold thee on thy throne,
Rock of ages, cleft for me,
Let me hide myself in thee.

241 And can it Be?

Charles Wesley.

Tune: Fillmore. L. M.

FINE.

1. { And can it be that I should gain An interest in the Sav-ior's blood?
   { Died he for me, who caused his pain? For me, who him to death pursued?

D. C. A-maz-ing love! how can it be That thou, my Lord, shouldst die for me?

D. C.

A-maz-ing love! how can it be That thou, my Lord, shouldst die for me?

2 He left the Father's throne above,—
  So free, so infinite his grace!—
Emptied himself of all but love,
  And bled for Adam's helpless race;
'Tis mercy all, immense and free,
For, O my God, it found out me!

3 Long my imprisoned spirit lay,
  Fast bound in sin and nature's night;
Thine eye diffused a quickening ray,
  I woke, the dungeon flamed with light:
My chains fell off, my heart was free,
I rose, went forth, and followed thee.

242 He Dies! The Friend.

Isaac Watts.

Tune: Duane Street. L. M. d.

1. He dies! the Friend of sinners dies! Lo! Salem's daughters weep around; A

FINE.

sol-emn dark-ness veils the skies, A sud-den trembling shakes the ground.

D. S. shed a thousand drops for you, A thousand drops of rich-er blood.

D. S.

Come, saints, and drop a tear or two For him who groaned beneath your load; He

2 Here's love and grief beyond degree,
  The Lord of glory dies for man!
But lo! what sudden joys we see,
  Jesus, the dead, revives again!
The rising God forsakes the tomb;
  In vain the tomb forbids his rise;
Cherubic legions guard him home,
  And shout him welcome to the skies.

243 Praise God, From Whom.

Tune above.

Praise God, from whom all blessings flow,
Praise him, all creatures here below;
Praise him above, ye heavenly host,
Praise Father, Son, and Holy Ghost.

199

244 Only Trust Him.

J. H. S.

Rev. J. H. STOCKTON.

1. Come, ev-'ry soul by sin oppressed, There's mercy with the Lord, And he will surely
2. For Je-sus shed his precious blood Rich blessings to bestow; Plunge now into the
3. Yes, Je-sus is the Truth, the Way, That leads you into rest; Believe in him with-
4. Come, then, and join this holy band, And on to glo-ry go, To dwell in that ce-

CHORUS.

give you rest, By trust-ing in his word. On - ly trust him, on-ly trust him,
crimson flood That washes white as snow. Come to Je-sus, come to Je - sus,
out de - lay, And you are ful-ly blest. Don't re-ject him, don't re-ject him,
les-tial land, Where joys immortal flow. I will trust him, I will trust him,

On-ly trust him now; He will save you, he will save you, He will save you now.
Come to Je-sus now; He will save you, he will save you, He will save you now.
Don't reject him now; He will save you, he will save you, He will save you now.
I will trust him now; He will save me, he will save me, He will save me now.

245 I Thirst, Thou Wounded Lamb.

Tune: SESSIONS. Opposite page.

1 I thirst, thou wounded Lamb of God,
To wash me in thy cleansing blood;
To dwell within thy wounds; then
  pain
Is sweet, and life or death is gain.

2 Take my poor heart, and let it be
Forever closed to all but thee;
Seal thou my breast, and let me wear
That pledge of love forever there.

3 How blest are they who still abide,
Close sheltered in thy bleeding side!
Who thence their life and strength de-
  rive,
And by thee move, and in thee live.

4 Hence our hearts melt, our eyes o'er-
  flow,
Our words are lost, nor will we know
Nor will we think of aught beside;
"My Lord, my Love is crucified."

N. L. ZINZENDORF. Tr. by J. WESLEY.

246

SAMUEL DAVIS.

Lord, I am Thine.

Tune: SESSIONS.

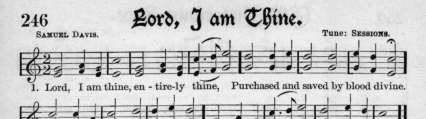

1. Lord, I am thine, en-tire-ly thine, Purchased and saved by blood divine.

With full consent thine I would be, And own thy sov - 'reign right in me.

2 Thine would I live, thine would I die,
Be thine through all eternity;
The vow is past beyond repeal,
And now I set the solemn seal.

3 Here, at the cross where flows the blood
That bought my guilty soul for God,
Thee, my new Master, now I call,
And consecrate to thee my all.

247   **Praise God, From Whom.**
Tune above.

Praise God, from whom all blessings
     flow,
Praise him, all creatures here below;
Praise him above, ye heavenly host,
Praise Father, Son, and Holy Ghost.

248

CHARLES WESLEY.

Arise, my Soul.

Tune: LENOX. H. M.

1 Arise, my soul, arise;
    Shake off thy guilty fears;
The bleeding Sacrifice
    In my behalf appears:
‖: Before the throne my Surety stands;:‖
My name is written on his hands.

2 He ever lives above,
    For me to intercede,
His all redeeming love,
    His precious blood to plead;
‖: His blood atoned for all our race, :‖
And sprinkles now the throne of grace.

3 To God I'm reconciled,
    His pardoning voice I hear;
He owns me for his child;
    I can no longer fear;
‖: With confidence I now draw nigh, :‖
    And Father, Abba, Father, cry.

249   **Blow Ye the Trumpet.**

1 Blow ye the trumpet, blow,
    The gladly solemn sound;
Let all the nations know,
    To earth's remotest bound,
‖: The year of jubilee is come; :‖
Return, ye ransomed sinners, home.

2 Jesus, our great High Priest,
    Hath full atonement made;
Ye weary spirits, rest;
    Ye mournful souls, be glad;
‖: The year of jubilee is come; :‖
Return, ye ransomed sinners, home.

3 Extol the Lamb of God,—
    The all-atoning Lamb;
Redemption in his blood
    Throughout the world proclaim;
‖: The year of jubilee is come; ‖
Return, ye ransomed sinners, home.

250 All-Victorious Love.

Isaac Watts.

Tune: St. Martin's. C. M.

1. Je - sus, thine all - vic - to - rious love Shed in my
2. O that in me the sa - cred fire Might now be -
3. O that it now from heaven might fall, And all my

heart a - broad: Then shall my feet no long - er rove,
gin to glow, Burn up the dross of base de - sire,
sins con - sume! Come, Ho - ly Ghost, for thee I call;

Root - ed and fixed in God.
And make the mountains flow!
Spir - it of burn - ing, come!

4 Refining fire, go through my heart;
   Illuminate my soul;
Scatter thy life through every part,
   And sanctify the whole.

5 My steadfast soul, from falling free,
   Shall then no longer move,
While Christ is all the world to me,
   And all my heart is love.

251 I Can, I Will, I Do.

(This Chorus can be used with hymns 224, 235, 246, and 250.)

1st Cho.—We're waiting at the mer-cy-seat, We're waiting at the mer-cy-seat,
2d Cho.— I can, I will, I do be-lieve, I can, I will, I do believe,

We're wait - ing at the mer - cy - seat, Where Je - sus an-swers prayer.
I can, I will, I do be - lieve That Je - sus died for me.

202

How Firm a Foundation.

GEORGE KEITH.   Tune: PORTUGUESE HYMN. 11s.   J. READING.

1 How firm a foundation, ye saints of
    the Lord!
  Is laid for your faith in his excellent
    word.
  What more can he say, than to you
    he hath said,—
  To you, who for refuge to Jesus have
    fled?

2 "Fear not, I am with thee, oh, be not
    dismayed,
  For I am thy God, I will still give
    thee aid;
  I'll strengthen thee, help thee, and
    cause thee to stand,
  Upheld by my gracious, omnipotent
    hand.

3 "The soul that on Jesus hath leaned
    for repose,
  I will not—I will not desert to his
    foes;
  That soul—though all hell should
    endeavor to shake,
  I'll never—no never—no never for-
    sake."

253   Sweet Hour of Prayer.
Key of D.

1 Sweet hour of prayer! sweet hour of
    prayer!
  That calls me from a world of care,
  And bids me at my Father's throne,
  Make all my wants and wishes known;
  In seasons of distress and grief,
  My soul has often found relief;
  And oft escaped the tempter's snare,
  By thy return, sweet hour of prayer.

2 Sweet hour of prayer! sweet hour of
    prayer!
  Thy wings shall my petitions bear
  To him whose truth and faithfulness
  Engage the waiting soul to bless;
  And since he bids me seek his face,
  Believe his word, and trust his grace,
  I'll cast on him my every care,
  And wait for thee, sweet hour of prayer.
                   W. W. WALFORD.

254   Oh, Turn Ye.
Tune above.

1 Oh, turn ye, oh, turn ye, for why will
    ye die,
  When God, in great mercy, is coming
    so nigh?
  Now Jesus invites you, the Spirit
    says, come,
  And angels are waiting to welcome
    you home.

2 In riches, in pleasure, what can you
    obtain,
  To soothe your affliction, or banish
    your pain?
  To bear up your spirit, when sum-
    moned to die,
  Or waft you to mansions of glory on
    high?

3 And now Christ is ready your souls
    to receive,
  Oh, how can you question if you will
    believe?
  If sin is your burden, why will you
    not come?
  'Tis you he bids welcome; he bids
    you come home.
                     J. HOPKINS.

255   Work, for the Night is Coming.
Key of F.

1 Work, for the night is coming,
    Work through the morning hours;
  Work while the dew is sparkling,
    Work 'mid springing flow'rs;
  Work, when the day grows brighter,
    Work in the glowing sun;
  Work, for the night is coming,
    When man's work is done.

2 Work, for the night is coming,
    Work through the sunny noon;
  Fill brightest hours with labor,
    Rest comes sure and soon;
  Give every flying minute,
    Something to keep in store;
  Work, for the night is coming,
    When man works no more.
                ANNIE L. WALKER.

256   **Jesus, Lover of my Soul.**

CHARLES WESLEY.   Tune, MARTIN. 7s.

FINE.   D. C.

1 Jesus, Lover of my soul,
   Let me to thy bosom fly,
While the nearer waters roll,
   While the tempest still is high.
Hide me, oh, my Savior, hide,
   Till the storm of life be past;
Safe into the haven guide,
   Oh, receive my soul at last.

2 Other refuge have I none,
   Hangs my helpless soul on thee,
Leave, ah, leave me not alone,
   Still support and comfort me.

All my trust on thee is stayed,
   All my help from thee I bring;
Cover my defenseless head
   With the shadow of thy wing.

3 Plenteous grace with thee is found—
   Grace to cover all my sin;
Let the healing streams abound;
   Make and keep me pure within.
Thou of life the fountain art,
   Freely let me take of thee:
Spring thou up within my heart;
   Rise to all eternity.

257   **How can I but Love Him?**

E. A. H.   ELISHA A. HOFFMAN.

1. What a pre-cious, pre-cious Friend is he! How can I but
2. He has ta-ken all my sins a-way, How can I but
3. He has rolled the bur-den from my soul, How can I but
4. He has filled my heart with per-fect peace, How can I but

love him? He has loved me from e-ter-ni-ty, My gra-cious Lord.
love him? He has taught me how to trust and pray, My gra-cious Lord.
love him? He has pu-ri-fied and made me whole, My gra-cious Lord.
love him? He has thrilled my soul with heav'nly bliss, My gra-cious Lord.

CHORUS.

{ How can I but love him? Wonderfully love him?
{ And for-ev-er love (*Omit* . . . .) Him, My gracious Lord.

258 Come, Thou Fount.

R. ROBINSON.

Tune, NETTLETON. 8, 7. D.

FINE.   D.C.

1 Come, Thou Fount of every blessing,
  Tune my heart to sing thy grace;
Streams of mercy, never ceasing,
  Call for songs of loudest praise.
Teach me some melodious sonnet,
  Sung by flaming tongues above;
Praise the mount—I'm fixed upon it—
  Mount of thy redeeming love.

2 Here I'll raise mine Ebenezer;
  Hither by thy help I'm come;
And I hope, by thy good pleasure,
  Safely to arrive at home.
Jesus sought me when a stranger,
  Wandering from the fold of God;
He, to rescue me from danger,
  Interposed his precious blood.

259 I Love Thy Kingdom, Lord.
Tune below.

1 I love thy kingdom, Lord,
  The house of thine abode,
The Church our blest Redeemer saved
  With his own precious blood.

2 I love thy Church, O God!
  Her walls before thee stand,
Dear as the apple of thine eye,
  And graven on thy hand.

3 Beyond my highest joy
  I prize her heavenly ways,
Her sweet communion, solemn vows,
  Her hymns of love and praise.

4 Sure as thy truth shall last,
  To Zion shall be given
The brightest glories earth can yield,
  And brighter bliss of heaven.
               TIMOTHY DWIGHT.

260 Soldiers of Christ, Arise.

CHARLES WESLEY.

Tune: LABAN. S. M.

1 Soldiers of Christ, arise,
  And put your armor on,
Strong in the strength which God
  Through his eternal Son.   [supplies

2 Strong in the Lord of hosts,
  And in his mighty power,
Who in the strength of Jesus trusts
  Is more than conqueror.

3 Stand, then, in his great might,
  With all his strength endued;
And take, to arm you for the fight,
  The panoply of God:

4 Till, having all things done,
  And all your conflicts passed,
You may o'ercome through Christ alone,
  And stand entire at last.

261 My Soul, be on Thy Guard.

1 My soul, be on thy guard,
  Ten thousand foes arise,
And hosts of sin are pressing hard
  To draw thee from the skies.

2 Oh, watch, and fight, and pray,
  The battle ne'er give o'er,
Renew it boldly every day,
  And help divine implore.

3 Ne'er think the victory won,
  Nor once at ease sit down;
Thine arduous work will not be done
  Till thou hast got the crown.

4 Fight on, my soul, till death
  Shall bring thee to thy God:
He'll take thee, at thy parting breath,
  Up to his blest abode.
               GEORGE HEATH.

262 What a Friend.

H. BONAR.   8s, 7s. D.   C. C. CONVERSE.

1. What a friend we have in Jesus, All our griefs and sins to bear! What a privilege to car-ry

D. S. All because we do not car-ry

FINE.   D. S.

Ev'ry thing to God in prayer! Oh, what peace we often forfeit, Oh, what needless pain we bear,
Ev'ry thing to God in prayer!

2 Have we trials and temptations?
　Is there trouble anywhere?
We should never be discouraged,
　Take it to the Lord in prayer.
Can we find a friend so faithful,
　Who will all our sorrows share?
Jesus knows our every weakness,
　Take it to the Lord in prayer.

3 Are we weak and heavy-laden,
　Cumbered with a load of care?
Precious Savior, still our refuge,—
　Take it to the Lord in prayer.
Do thy friends despise, forsake thee?
　Take it to the Lord in prayer;
In his arms he'll take and shield thee,
　Thou wilt find a solace there.

BY PERMISSION.

263 Cleansing Wave.

PHOEBE PALMER.   MRS. J. F. KNAPP.

CHORUS.

1 Oh, now I see the cleansing wave!
　The fountain deep and wide;
Jesus, my Lord, mighty to save,
　Points to his wounded side.

CHO.—The cleansing stream, I see, I see,
　I plunge, and oh, it cleanseth me!
Oh, praise the Lord! it cleanseth me!
　It cleanseth me—yes, cleanseth me.

2 I rise to walk in heaven's own light,
　Above the world of sin, 　　[white,
With heart made pure and garments
　And Christ enthroned within.

3 Amazing grace! 'tis heaven below
　To feel the blood applied;
And Jesus, only Jesus, know,
　My Jesus crucified.

BY PERMISSION.

264 Stand up for Jesus.

G. DUFFIELD.   Tune: WEBB. 7, 6.

D. C.

1 Stand up, stand up for Jesus,
    Ye soldiers of the cross;
Lift high his royal banner,
    It must not suffer loss;

From victory unto victory
    His army shall he lead,
Till every foe is vanquished
    And Christ is Lord indeed.

2 Stand up, stand up for Jesus,
    The strife will not be long;
This day the noise of battle,
    The next the victor's song:
To him that overcometh,
    A crown of life shall be;
He with the King of glory
    Shall reign eternally.

265   The Morning Light is Breaking.

1 The morning light is breaking;
    The darkness disappears;
The sons of earth are waking
    To penitential tears;
Each breeze that sweeps the ocean
    Brings tidings from afar,
Of nations in commotion,
    Prepared for Zion's war.

2 Blest river of salvation,
    Pursue thine onward way;
Flow thou to every nation,
    Nor in thy richness stay:
Stay not till all the lowly
    Triumphant reach their home:
Stay not till all the holy
    Proclaim, "The Lord is come!"
                        S. F. SMITH.

266   O Youth With Hearts Aspiring.

1 O youth with hearts aspiring,
    What visions greet your eye!
What fields for noble conquest!
    What growth and victory!
How high your heavenly calling—
    The Christ-like life to win,
The prize of holy manhood,
    The overthrow of sin!

2 O youth with hearts aspiring,
    Embrace your heavenly call;
Your standard is perfection,
    Your Christ the Lord of all.
Win others to his standard,
    Enlarge the youthful throng,
Till all the earth, in Jesus,
    Can sing redemption's song.
                    REV. DWIGHT M. PRATT.

267 To-Day the Savior Calls.

SAMUEL FRANCIS SMITH.   DR. LOWELL MASON.

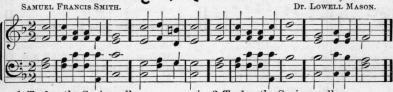

1 To-day the Savior calls;
    Ye wand'rers, come;
O ye benighted souls,
    Why longer roam?

2 To-day the Savior calls;
    Oh, hear him now;
Within these sacred walls
    To Jesus bow.

3 To-day the Saviour calls;
    For refuge fly;
The storm of justice falls,
    And death is nigh.

4 The Spirit calls to-day;
    Yield to his power,
Oh, grieve him not away,
    'Tis mercy's hour.

Revive us Again.

WM. P. MACKAY. J. J. HUSBAND.

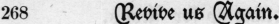

1. We praise thee, O God! for the Son of thy love, For Je-sus who died and is now gone a-bove.

REFRAIN.

Hal - le - lu-jah! thine the glo - ry; Hal - le - lu-jah! a - men! Re-vive us a - gain.

2 We praise thee, O God! for thy Spirit of light,
Who has shown us our Savior and scattered our night.

3 All glory and praise to the Lamb that was slain,
Who has borne all our sins, and has cleansed every stain.

4 Revive us again; fill each heart with thy love;
May each soul be rekindled with fire from above.

269 # Guide me, Great Jehovah.

WILLIAM WILLIAMS. Tune: ZION. 8, 7, 4.

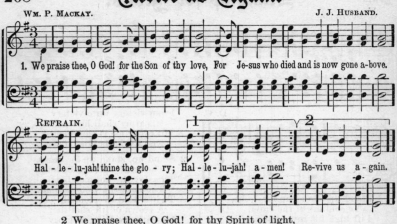

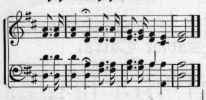

3 When I tread the verge of Jordan,
Bid my anxious fears subside;
Bear me through the swelling current;
Land me safe on Canaan's side:
Songs of praises
I will ever give to Thee.

270 **Welcome, Dear Redeemer.**

1 Welcome, welcome, dear Redeemer,
Welcome to this heart of mine;
Lord, I make a full surrender,
Every power and thought be thine;
Thine entirely,
Through eternal ages thine.

2 Known to all to be thy mansion,
Earth and hell will disappear;
Or in vain attempt possession,
When they find the Lord is near;
Shout, O Zion!
Shout, ye saints! the Lord is here.

1 Guide me, O thou great Jehovah,
Pilgrim through this barren land:
I am weak, but thou art mighty;
Hold me with thy powerful hand:
Bread of heaven,
Feed me till I want no more

2 Open now the crystal fountain,
Whence the healing waters flow;
Let the fiery, cloudy pillar,
Lead me all my journey through:
Strong Deliverer,
Be thou still my strength and shield.

271 Awake, my Soul.

S. MEDLEY.

Tune: LOVING KINDNESS. L. M.

1 Awake, my soul, in joyful lays,
And sing thy great Redeemer's praise;
He justly claims a song from me;
His loving kindness, oh, how free!

2 He saw me ruined by the fall,
Yet loved me, notwithstanding all;
He saved me from my lost estate:
His loving kindness, oh, how great!

3 Though mighty hosts of cruel foes,
Though earth and hell my way oppose,
He safely leads my soul along;
His loving kindness, oh, how strong!

4 So when I pass death's gloomy vale,
And all my mortal powers must fail,
Oh, may my last, expiring breath
His loving kindness sing in death.

272 More Love to Thee.
Key of Db

1 More love to Thee, O Christ!
    More love to thee!
Hear thou the prayer I make
    On bended knee;
This is my earnest plea,—
More love, O Christ, to thee,
    More love to thee!

2 Once earthly joy I craved,
    Sought peace and rest;
Now thee alone I seek,
    Give what is best:
This all my prayer shall be,—
More love, O Christ, to thee,
    More love to thee!

3 Let sorrow do its work,
    Send grief and pain;
Sweet are thy messengers,
    Sweet their refrain,
When they can sing with me,—
More love, O Christ, to thee,
    More love to thee!

4 Then shall my latest breath
    Whisper thy praise;
This be the parting cry
    My heart shall raise,—
This still its prayer shall be,—
More love, O Christ, to thee,
    More love to thee!

E. P. PRENTICE.

273 Nearer, my God, to Thee.
Key of G.

1 Nearer, my God, to thee,
    Nearer to thee!
E'en thou it be a cross
    That raiseth me;.
Still all my song shall be—
Nearer, my God, to thee!
    Nearer to thee.

2 Though like a wanderer,
    The sun gone down;
Darkness be over me,
    My rest a stone;
Yet in my dreams I'd be—
Nearer, my God, to thee!
    Nearer to thee!

3 There let the way appear,
    Steps unto heaven:
All that thou sendest me,
    In mercy given;
Angels to beckon me—
Nearer, my God to thee!
    Nearer to thee!

4 Or, if on joyful wing,
    Cleaving the sky,
Sun, moon, and stars forgot,
    Upward I fly,
Still all my song shall be—
Nearer, my God, to thee!
    Nearer to thee!

SARAH F. ADAMS.

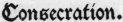

274

Consecration.

Mrs. MARY D. JAMES.

Mrs. JOS. F. KNAPP.

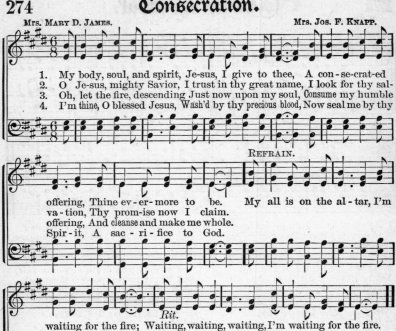

1. My body, soul, and spirit, Je-sus, I give to thee, A con-se-crat-ed
2. O Je-sus, mighty Savior, I trust in thy great name, I look for thy sal-
3. Oh, let the fire, descending Just now upon my soul, Consume my humble
4. I'm thine, O blessed Jesus, Wash'd by thy precious blood, Now seal me by thy

REFRAIN.

offering, Thine ev-er-more to be. My all is on the al-tar, I'm
va-tion, Thy prom-ise now I claim.
offering, And cleanse and make me whole.
Spir-it, A sac-ri-fice to God.

Rit.

waiting for the fire; Waiting, waiting, waiting, I'm waiting for the fire.

FROM "NOTES OF JOY." BY PER.

275 He Leadeth Me. Key, D.

1 He leadeth me! oh! blessed thought,
Oh! words with heavenly comfort fraught;
Whate'er I do, where'er I be,
Still 'tis God's hand that leadeth me.

REF.—He leadeth me! he leadeth me!
By his own hand he leadeth me;
His faithful follower I would be,
For by his hand he leadeth me.

2 Sometimes 'mid scenes of deepest gloom,
Sometimes where Eden's bowers bloom,
By waters still, o'er troubled sea,
Still 'tis his hand that leadeth me.

3 Lord, I would clasp thy hand in mine,
Nor ever mummur nor repine—
Content, whatever lot I see—
Since 'tis my God that leadeth me.

4 And when my task on earth is done,
When, by thy grace the victory's won,
E'en death's cold wave I will not flee,
Since God through Jordan leadeth me.
J. H. GILMORE.

276 Take the Name of Jesus. Key, A♭.

1 Take the name of Jesus with you,
Child of sorrow and of woe;
It will joy and comfort give you,
Take it, then, where'er you go.

CHO.—Precious name, O how sweet,
Hope of earth and joy of heaven;
Precious name, O how sweet,
Hope of earth and joy of heaven;

2 Take the name of Jesus ever,
As a shield from every snare;
If temptations round you gather,
Breathe that holy name in prayer.

3 Oh! the precious name of Jesus;
How it thrills our souls with joy,
When his loving arms receive us,
And his songs our tongues employ.

4 At the name of Jesus bowing,
Falling prostrate at his feet,
King of kings in heav'n we'll crown him,
When our journey is complete.
Mrs. LYDIA BAXTER.

Oh, Could I Speak.

Tune: ARIEL. C. H. M.

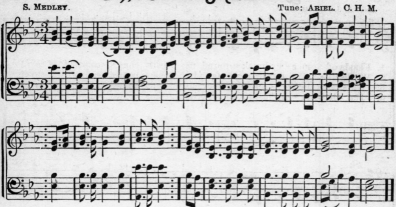

1 Oh, could I speak the matchless worth,
Oh, could I sound the glories forth
    Which in my Savior shine,
I'd soar and touch the heavenly strings,
And vie with Gabriel while he sings,
    ‖:In notes almost divine. :‖

2 I'd sing the precious blood he spilt,
My ransom from the dreadful guilt,
    Of sin and wrath divine!
I'd sing his glorious righteousness,
In which all perfect heavenly dress
    ‖:My soul shall ever shine. :‖

3 Well—the delightful day will come,
When my dear Lord will bring me home,
    And I shall see his face:
Then with my Savior, Brother, Friend,
A blest eternity I'll spend,
    ‖:Triumphant in his grace. :‖

278 I Believe Jesus Saves.
Tune: SWEET BYE AND BYE.
Key of G.

1 I am coming to Jesus for rest,
    Rest, such as the purified know;
My soul is athirst to be blest,
    To be washed and made whiter than
    snow.

CHORUS.

I believe Jesus saves,
    And his blood washes whiter than snow,
I believe Jesus saves,
    And his blood washes whiter than snow.

2 In coming, my sin I deplore,
    My weakness and poverty show;
I long to be saved evermore,
    To be washed and made whiter than
    snow.

3 To Jesus, I give up my all,
    Every treasure and Idol I know;
For his fullness of blessing I call,
    Till his blood washes whiter than snow.

4 I am trusting in Jesus alone,
    Trusting now his salvation to know;
And his blood doth so fully atone,
    I am washed and made whiter than
    snow.

5 My heart is in raptures of love,
    Love, such as the ransomed ones know;
I am strengthened with might from above
    I am washed and made whiter than
    snow.

Rev. WM. MCDONALD.
FROM "SONGS OF JOY AND GLADNESS." BY PER.

279 O Beulah Land.
Key of G.

1 I've reached the land of corn and wine,
    And all its riches freely mine,
    Here shines undimm'd one blissful day,
    For all my night has pass'd away.

CHORUS.

O Beulah Land, sweet Beulah Land,
    As on thy highest mount I stand,
    I look away across the sea,
    Where mansions are prepared for me,
    And view the shining glory shore,
    My heav'n, my home, for evermore!

2 My Savior comes and walks with me,
    And sweet communion here have we;
    He gently leads me by his hand,
    For this is heaven's border-land.

3 The zephyrs seem to float to me
    Sweet sounds of heaven's melody,
    As angels with the white-rob'd throng
    Join in the sweet redemption song.

BY PER. OF J. J. HOOD, OWNER OF COPYRIGHT. E. P. STITES.

280 Jesus Comes to Save.

Rev. A. J. Hough.　　　　　　　　　　　　　　J. E. Hall.

1. Floods of mer-cy break a-round us, Je-sus comes, comes to save!
2. While like rain our tears are fall-ing, Je-sus comes, comes to save!
3. Glo-rious light is dawning o'er us, Je-sus comes, comes to save!
4. Hal-le-lu-jah! saints are sing-ing, Je-sus comes, comes to save!

FINE.

Fet-ters fall that long have bound us, Je-sus comes, comes to save!
While these souls for help are call-ing, Je-sus comes, comes to save!
And the way grows bright be-fore us, Je-sus comes, comes to save!
Heaven with joy-ous song is ring-ing, Je-sus comes, comes to save!

D.S. Hal-le-lu-jah! hal-le-lu-jah! Je-sus comes, comes to save.

CHORUS.　　　　　　　　　　　　　　　　　　　D. S

Hal-le-lu-jah! joy-ful sto-ry, Je-sus comes, the King of glo-ry!

BY PER. OF R. E. HUDSON.

281 O Weary Wand'rer.

Tune: ALMOST PERSUADED.

1 O weary wand'rer, dark night comes on,
When slighted mercy will be with-
　The Spirit strive no more, [drawn:—
　Christ gives his pleadings o'er,
　Closed then shall be the door;
　　Thy doom, despair.

2 O weary wand'rer, Jesus still pleads;
For you he suffers, for you he bleeds.
　O let his love constrain,
　Nor let him bleed in vain;
　Hark! hark! he calls again,
　　"O wand'rer, come."

3 O weary wand'rer, why still delay?
Christ waits to save you—save you to-
　Fast falls the eventide; [day;
　Soon, soon you must decide;
　For you he bled and died
　　On Calvary!

4 O weary wand'rer, see loved ones stand,
All saved in heaven, a happy band.
　Come, join them on that shore;
　Where death shall part no more;
　Wide open stands the door,
　　O wand'rer, come.

I Baltzell and E. D. Mund.

282 Come, Ye Sinners.

Joseph Hart.

Tune, Greenville, 8, 7, 4.

1 Come, ye sinners, poor and needy,
  Weak and wounded, sick and sore;
Jesus ready stands to save you,
  Full of pity, love, and power:
    ‖:He is able,:‖
  He is willing: doubt no more.

2 Now, ye needy, come and welcome;
  God's free bounty glorify;
True belief and true repentance,
  Every grace that brings you nigh,
    ‖:Without money,:‖
  Come to Jesus Christ and buy.

3 Let not conscience make you linger,
  Nor of fitness fondly dream;
All the fitness He requireth
  Is to feel your need of him,
    ‖:This he gives you;:‖
  'Tis the Spirit's glimmering beam.

4 Come, ye weary, heavy-laden,
  Bruised and mangled by the fall;
If you tarry till you're better,
  You will never come at all;
    ‖:Not the righteous—:‖
  Sinners Jesus came to call.

5 Agonizing in the garden,
  Your Redeemer prostrate lies;
On the bloody tree behold him!
  Hear him cry, before he dies,
    ‖:"It is finished!":‖
  Sinners, will not this suffice?

6 Lo! the incarnate God, ascending,
  Pleads the merit of his blood;
Venture on him, venture freely;
  Let no other trust intrude
    ‖:None but Jesus::‖
  Can do helpless sinners good.

283 Turn to the Lord. 8, 7.

Jeremiah Ingalls.

Fine.

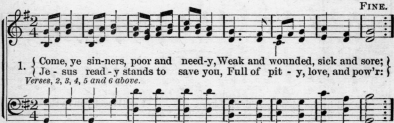

1. { Come, ye sin-ners, poor and need-y, Weak and wounded, sick and sore; }
   { Je-sus read-y stands to save you, Full of pit-y, love, and pow'r: }
   Verses, 2, 3, 4, 5 and 6 above.

D.C. Glo-ry, hon-or, and sal-va-tion, Christ the Lord has come to reign.

Chorus.

D.C.

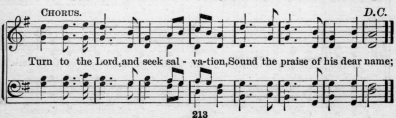

Turn to the Lord, and seek sal-va-tion, Sound the praise of his dear name;

My Happy Home.

Anon.

E. O. EXCELL.

1. Je - ru - sa - lem, my hap-py home, Oh, how I long for thee!
2. Thy walls are all of precious stone Most glo-rious to be - hold;
3. Thy gar-dens and thy pleasant streams My stud-y long have been—
4. Reach down, reach down thine arms of grace, And cause me to as - cend

When will my sor-rows have an end? Thy joys, when shall I see?
Thy gates are rich-ly set with pearl, Thy streets are paved with gold.
Such sparkling gems by hu - man sight Have nev - er yet been seen.
Where con-gre - ga-tions ne'er break up, And prais - es nev - er end.

CHORUS.

I will meet you in the Cit-y of the new Je - ru - sa-lem, I am

washed in the blood of the Lamb,...... I will meet you in the Cit-y
washed in the blood, in the blood of the Lamb,

of the New Je-ru - sa-lem, I am washed in the blood of the Lamb.

285 Sun of My Soul.

JOHN KEBLE.

Tune, HURSLEY. L. M.

1. Sun of my soul, thou Sav-ior dear, It is not night if thou be near:
2. When the soft dews of kind-ly sleep My wearied eye-lids gen-tly steep,
3. A-bide with me from morn till eve, For without thee I can-not live;
4. If some poor wand'ring child of thine Have spurned today the voice divine,

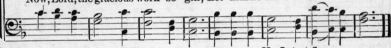

O may no earthborn cloud a - rise To hide thee from thy servant's eyes.
Be my last thot', how sweet to rest For-ev-er on my Sav-ior's breast.
A-bide with me when night is nigh, For without thee I dare not die.
Now, Lord, the gracious work be-gin; Let him no more lie down in sin.

---

286 My Days are Gliding.
Key of G.

1 My days are gliding swiftly by,
  And I, a pilgrim stranger,
Would not detain them as they fly,
Those hours of toil and danger.

CHORUS.—
  For, O, we stand on Jordan's strand,
  Our friends are passing over,
And just before the shining shore
We may almost discover.

2 Should coming days be cold and dark,
We need not cease our singing;
That perfect rest naught can molest,
Where golden harps are ringing.

3 Let sorrows rudest tempest blow,
Each chord on earth to sever;[home,
Our King says, "Come," and there's our
Forever, O, forever!

DAVID NELSON.

---

287 My Latest Sun.
Key of C.

1 My latest sun is sinking fast,
  My race is nearly run;
My strongest trials now are past,
  My triumph is begun.

CHORUS.—
  O come, angel band,
  Come and around me stand,
‖:O, bear me away on your snowy wings,
  To my immortal home.:‖

2 I know I'm nearing the holy ranks,
Of friends and kindred dear [banks,
For I brush the dews on Jordan's
The crossing must be near.

3 I've almost gained my heavenly home,
My spirit loudly sings;
The holy ones behold they come!
I hear the noise of wings.

JEFFERSON HASCALL.

---

288 I'm Going Home.
Rev. WM. HUNTER.
WM. MILLER.

1. { My heav'nly home is bright and fair; Nor pain, nor death can enter there:
   { Its glitt'ring tow'rs the sun outshine; That heav'nly mansion shall be mine.

CHO. { I'm go-ing home, I'm go-ing home, I'm go-ing home to die no more!
     { To die no more, to die no more, I'm go-ing home to die no more!

2 My Father's house is built on high,
Far, far above the starry sky;
When from this earthly prison free,
That heavenly mansion mine shall be.

3 Let others seek a home below, [flow;
Which flames devour, or waves o'er-
Be mine a happier lot to own
A heavenly mansion near the throne.

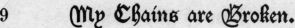

My Chains are Broken.

ELISHA A. HOFFMAN.   REV. B. C. OYLER.

1. {Now the chains of sin are bro-ken, I am free, I'm free;
   Christ the word of power has spok-en Un-to me, to me.}

2. {Soon as I by faith re-ceived him Fled the night, the night;
   In the mo-ment I be-lieved him Came the light, the light.}

3. {All the fet-ters that op-pressed me Now are riv'n, are riv'n;
   With his pre-cious love he blessed me, This to me is heav'n.}

4. {I will tell the won-drous sto-ry Of his grace and love;
   He has filled my soul with glo-ry; Praise the Lord a-bove!}

CHORUS.

Hal - le - lu - jah! hal - le - lu - jah! Je - sus died for
me; Hal - le - lu - jah! hal - le - lu - jah! I am free, I'm free.

USED BY PER. OF E. A. HOFFMAN, OWNER OF COPYRIGHT.

---

290   **Enter by the Blood of Jesus.**
(Tune, NOTHING BUT THE BLOOD.)
Key of G.

1 The Holiest Place stands open wide,
    Enter by the blood of Jesus;
The shadowing veil now hangs aside,
    Enter by the blood of Jesus.

CHO.—Beyond the second veil
    Pure love and joy prevail,
      God's promise ne'er can fail,
    Enter by the blood of Jesus.

2 Enter now this holiest place
    Enter by the blood of Jesus;
Here Christ reveals his shining face,
    Enter by the blood of Jesus.

3 Now by faith you may prevail,
    Enter by the blood of Jesus;
Pass beyond the second veil,
    Enter by the blood of Jesus.

REV. J. B. FOOTE.

---

291   **The Solid Rock.**
Key of G.

1 My hope is built on nothing less
Than Jesus' blood and righteousness:
I dare not trust the sweetest frame,
But wholly lean on Jesus' name.

CHO.—On Christ, the Solid Rock, I stand,
    All other ground is sinking sand.

2 When darkness veils his lovely face,
I rest on his unchanging grace:
In every high and stormy gale,
My anchor holds within the vail.

3 When he shall come with trumpet
    sound,
Oh, may I then in him be found;
Drest in his righteousness alone,
Faultless to stand before the throne.

EDWARD MOTT

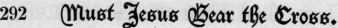

292 Must Jesus Bear the Cross.

THOS. SHEPHERD.   Tune, MAITLAND.   C. M.

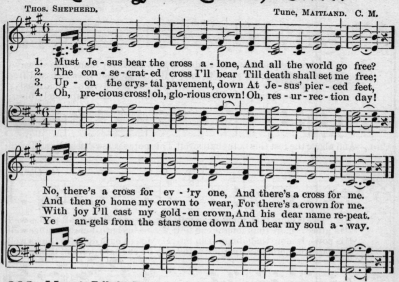

1. Must Je-sus bear the cross a-lone, And all the world go free?
2. The con-se-crat-ed cross I'll bear Till death shall set me free;
3. Up-on the crys-tal pavement, down At Je-sus' pier-ced feet,
4. Oh, pre-cious cross! oh, glo-rious crown! Oh, res-ur-rec-tion day!

No, there's a cross for ev-'ry one, And there's a cross for me.
And then go home my crown to wear, For there's a crown for me.
With joy I'll cast my gold-en crown, And his dear name re-peat.
Ye an-gels from the stars come down And bear my soul a-way.

293   I Love to Tell the Story.
Key of A♭

1 I love to tell the story
  Of unseen things above,
  Of Jesus and his glory,
  Of Jesus and his love.
  I love to tell the story,
  Because I know 'tis true;
  It satisfies my longings
  As nothing else can do.

CHO.—I love to tell the story,
    'Twill be my theme in glory,
    To tell the old, old story
    Of Jesus and his love.

2 I love to tell the story:
  More wonderful it seems
  Then all the golden fancies
  Of all our golden dreams.
  I love to tell the story,
  It did so much for me;
  And that is just the reason
  I tell it now to thee.

3 I love to tell the story,
  For those who know it best
  Seem hungering and thirsting
  To hear it like the rest.
  And when, in scenes of glory,
  I sing the new, new song,
  'Twill be the old, old story
  That I have loved so long.
                    CATHERINE HANKEY.
            By permission.

294   Marching to Zion.
Key of G.

1 Come, ye that love the Lord,
    And let your joys be known,
  Join in a song with sweet accord,
  Join in a song with sweet accord,
    And thus surround the throne,
    And thus surround the throne.

CHO.—We're marching to Zion,
    Beautiful, beautiful Zion,
  We're marching upward to Zion,
    The beautiful city of God.

2 Let those refuse to sing
    Who never knew our God;
  But children of the heav'nly King,
  But children of the heav'nly King,
    May speak their joys abroad,
    May speak their joys abroad.

3 The hill of Zion yields,
    A thousand sacred sweets,
  Before we reach the heav'nly fields,
  Before we reach the heav'nly fields,
    Or walk the golden streets,
    Or walk the golden streets.

4 Then let our songs abound,
    And every tear be dry,   [ground,
  We're marching through Immanuel's
  We're marching through Immanuel's
    To fairer worlds on high,   [ground,
    To fairer worlds on high.
                        ISAAC WATTS.

217

295 Jesus hath Done all Things Well.

ELISHA A. HOFFMAN.　　　　　　　Arr. by M. L. McPHAIL.

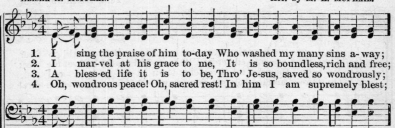

1. I sing the praise of him to-day Who washed my many sins a-way;
2. I mar-vel at his grace to me, It is so boundless, rich and free;
3. A bless-ed life it is to be, Thro' Je-sus, saved so wondrously;
4. Oh, wondrous peace! Oh, sacred rest! In him I am supremely blest;

CHO.—And above the rest this note shall swell, This note shall swell, this note shall swell;

D.C. for Chorus.

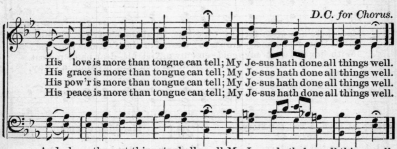

His love is more than tongue can tell; My Je-sus hath done all things well.
His grace is more than tongue can tell; My Je-sus hath done all things well.
His pow'r is more than tongue can tell; My Je-sus hath done all things well.
His peace is more than tongue can tell; My Je-sus hath done all things well.

And above the rest this note shall swell, My Je-sus hath done all things well.

296　　　　　　　Tune above.

Praise God, from whom all blessings
　　flow;
Praise him, all creatures here below;
Praise him above, ye heavenly host;
Praise Father, Son and Holy Ghost.

CHORUS.
And above the rest this note shall swell,
This note shall swell, this note shall swell;
And above the rest this note shall swell,
　My Jesus hath done all things well.

297　　　Tune, AVON. C. M. No. 209.

To Father, Son, and Holy Ghost,
　The God whom we adore,
Be glory, as it was, is now,
And shall be evermore!

　　　　　TATE and BRADY.

298　Tune, BOYLSTON. S. M. No. 232.

To God, the Father, Son,
　And Spirit, One in Three,
Be glory, as it was, is now,
　And shall forever be.

　　　　　JOHN WESLEY.

299　Tune, LENOX. H. M. No. 248.

To God, the Father's throne
　Your highest honors raise;
Glory to God, the Son;
　To God, the Spirit, praise:
With all our powers, eternal King,
Thy everlasting praise we sing.

　　　　　ISAAC WATTS. Alt.

300　　Tune, TOPLADY. 7. 6l. No. 240.

Praise the name of God most high;
Praise him, all below the sky;
Praise him, all ye heavenly host,
Father, Son, and Holy Ghost!
As through countless ages past,
Evermore his praise shall last.

　　　　　Unknown.

301　Tune, AMERICA. 6. 4. No. 182.

To God, the Father, Son,
And Spirit, Three in One,
　All praise be given!
Crown him in every song;
To him your hearts belong:
Let all his praise prolong,
　On earth, in heaven!

　　　　　EDWIN F. HATFIELD

302 **Lord, Dismiss Us.**

Tune, SICILY.

W. SHIRLEY.

1. Lord, dis- miss us with thy bless-ing, Fill our hearts with joy and peace;
2. Thanks we give and ad- o- ra- tion, For thy gos- pel's joy-ful sound;
3. So, when-e'er the sig-nal's giv- en Us from earth to call a- way,

Let us each thy love pos- sess-ing, Triumph in re- deem-ing grace.
May the fruits of thy sal- va- tion In our hearts and lives a- bound.
Borne on an- gels' wings to heav-en, Glad the sum-mons to o- bey,

O re-fresh us! O re-fresh us! Trav'ling thro' this wil-der- ness.
May thy presence, may thy presence With us ev- er-more be found.
May we read-y, may we read- y, Rise and reign in end-less day.

303 **Praise God from Whom.**

THOMAS KEN.

Tune, OLD HUNDRED. L. M.

Praise God from whom all blessings flow; Praise him, all creatures here be-low;

Praise him a- bove, ye heav'nly host; Praise Father, Son, and Ho-ly Ghost.

God be with You.

J. E. RANKIN, D. D.

W. G. TOMER.

1. God be with you till we meet a-gain, By his counsels guide up-
2. God be with you till we meet a-gain, 'Neath his wings protecting,
3. God be with you till we meet a-gain, When life's per-ils thick con-
4. God be with you till we meet a-gain, Keep love's banner floating

hold you, With his sheep se-cure-ly fold you, God be with you
hide you, Dai-ly man-na still pro-vide you, God be with you
found you, Put his arms un-fail-ing round you, God be with you
o'er you, Smite death's threat'ning wave before you, God be with you

CHORUS.

till we meet a-gain. Till we meet, till we meet,
Till we meet, till we meet, till we meet,

Till we meet at Je-sus' feet, Till we meet,..........
Till we meet at Je-sus' feet, Till we meet, till we meet,

till we meet, God be with you till we meet a-gain.
till we meet, till we meet, God be with you till we meet a-gain.

Topical Index.

Index.

Titles in CAPITALS; first lines in Roman; metrical tunes in *Italics*.

Pentecostal Hymns.

Pentecostal Hymns.